Because she felt sorry for her employer, Greg Lindley, whose marriage had ended so unhappily, Margret was anxious for him to marry Laura Spencer whom he loved and who was so suitable. But it didn't seem likely that Laura would look at Greg as long as his cousin Carl was around. Would it make the situation better or worse if Margret tried to encourage Carl herself?

Books you will enjoy
by FLORA KIDD

BEYOND CONTROL

Expediency had been the only reason for Kate marrying Sean Kierly, and immediately after the wedding he had taken himself off and for the next two years she had seen and heard nothing of him. Now, in Ireland, she had met him again—and the natural, sensible thing to do seemed to be to dissolve the marriage. But Kate had fallen in love with Sean at first sight and she was still reluctant to divorce him. Yet what was the point of clinging to a man who so obviously didn't love her?

WIFE BY CONTRACT

Her marriage to Damien Nikerios had brought Teri position, as the wife of an immensely rich Greek shipping magnate, money, beautiful homes in Greece—and the humiliation of knowing that Damien had only married her as a cover-up for his affair with his father's wife. Yet for the sake of her family Teri had put up with it. But for how long could she stand it?

THE SILKEN BOND

Eight years after she had last seen him—and loved him—Lyn met Joel Morgan again, and it seemed she now had a second chance when this time he asked her to marry him. But what was the use, when she knew he still did not love her, and that if she accepted her marriage would be forever haunted by the ghost of his lovely dead wife Sabrina?

THE ARRANGED MARRIAGE

To please her godmother, Roselle had agreed to go into the marriage the old lady had arranged for her with her grandson Léon Chauvigny—but each of them had commitments elsewhere and the marriage had never been a real one; certainly not a loving one. Now the time had come to end it once and for all. Or had it?

PERSONAL AFFAIR

BY

FLORA KIDD

MILLS & BOON LIMITED

15–16 BROOK'S MEWS

LONDON W1A 1DR

First published 1981
Australian copyright 1981
Philippine copyright 1981
This edition 1981

© Flora Kidd 1981

ISBN 0 263 73605 9

Set in Monophoto Baskerville 11 on 13 pt.

Made and printed in Great Britain by
Richard Clay (The Chaucer Press) Ltd,
Bungay, Suffolk

CHAPTER ONE

THE night was calm and dark. From the window of her bedroom on the second floor of the old timbered house Margret Randall could see a grey haze of fog creeping in from the ocean, slithering over the narrow strait of water which separated Lindley's Point from the island known as Hog's Back. There were no lights except the light streaming forth from her window. There were none of the usual night noises either. No crickets chanted in the undergrowth, no ducks squawked among the reeds. She couldn't even hear the soft sigh of the waves on the shore.

Suddenly her ears pricked. What was that? The throb of an engine? It seemed to be coming from the water, yet it was not the sort of night for a boat to be trying to enter the narrow strait, which was foul with rocks. She listened hard. No sound. The noise must have been a figment of her imagination after all, the result of reading an exciting mystery story. It was time she went to sleep. Leaving the window slightly open at the bottom, she padded back to bed, plumped up the pillows, checked that the time was a quarter past one in the morning, wound up the alarm clock after setting it for seven-thirty, lay down on the bed and turned off the bedside lamp.

As the darkness swept around her she heard the noise again, coming through the opening of the window. It was much louder now and was definitely recognisable as a marine engine. Not a fishing boat, it wasn't powerful enough for that, more like a yacht's auxiliary engine, and the sound was being amplified as it was bounced back from the cliffs of the island.

Curiosity getting the better of her resolve to go to sleep, she pushed aside the bedclothes, slid off the bed and went back to the window to peer down in the direction of the noise. The fog was playing tricks, coming and going so that sometimes the shape of the island could be seen, humped darkly against the dark sky, and sometimes it was invisible, drowned in the thickness of the grey haze.

The sound of the engine was loud now and the pitch had changed. It whined eerily as it was put into neutral gear and Margret guessed that the boat was about to stop. Another sound, echoed back from the island, a splash as something fell into the water. An anchor? Margret strained to see through the wisps of fog. Two small lights, one red and one green like two dissimilar eyes, winked at her from the strait. They were the navigation lights of the boat. The engine was cut and all was silent again. The navigation lights went out and a softer, more mellow light glowed through the windows of a cabin. Slowly they became fainter as the fog thickened and eventually smothered them.

Shivering a little as the thick damp air wafted in through the window and fingered her face and throat, Margret turned away and went back to bed. But not to sleep. She was disturbed by the presence of the boat in the strait. Both Nelson and Millie White, who kept an eye on the house at Lindley's Point for its owner, had told her that very few pleasure yachts ever came into the small anchorage because the entrance to it was difficult without local knowledge. So whoever was on the boat had been to this place before. Why had they come in the night? All the stories she had heard about the drug smuggling which went on along this particular stretch of the coast rushed into her mind to torment her. Unable to rest, she left the bed again and went to the window.

Her blood seemed to freeze in her veins because down there on the shore was a light, bobbing about. Someone was moving about with a flashlight. Someone from the boat come ashore in a dinghy and who was now approaching the house. Her nerves twanging because, apart from the children, Heather and Jamie, she was alone in the house, she groped her way in the dark from the room and down the stairs into the small front hallway. There she slid the bolt across the top of the front door and attached the chain. It wouldn't do for the house to be broken into while she was in charge of it; there were too many valuable ornaments and antique pieces of furniture scattered about the place.

From the hallway she went into the large living

room, intending to go through to the kitchen and
make sure the back door was secure too. She was
halfway across the room, still feeling her way in the
darkness, when she heard a sound coming from the
kitchen. At once she froze where she was, her hand
closing round the top rung of one of the old ladderbacked chairs which were set round the dining
table. Holding her breath, she listened again.
Someone was sliding open the kitchen window
which she must have left slightly open as usual.

There was a thudding sound as if someone had
jumped down on to the floor, then a switch clicked
and light flooded the kitchen. Rubber soles
squeaked on the vinyl floor covering. There was a
sighing sound as the fridge door was opened. Margret let out her breath, gathered all her courage together and called out,

'Who's there?'

There was a moment's silence, then the fridge
door thumped shut. A figure appeared in the doorway leading to the kitchen. Another switch clicked
and light swirled around the living room. The man
who had switched on the light was tall and was
wearing bright yellow oilskin trousers and jacket.
Drops of water glistened on the oilskins and on his
sun-bleached hair. His broad, square-chinned face
had been tanned by sun and wind, making his eyes
seem very blue. He was as surprised to see Margret
as she was to see him and stared at her incredu-
lously. Then slowly his expression changed and the
corner of his mouth lifted in a slight smile.

'Nice of you to come down and welcome me,' he said.

Feeling very vulnerable in her thin cotton shirt-like nightgown which clung to her shape, leaving little to the imagination, Margret folded her arms in front of her and returned his stare coldly.

'I didn't come down to make you welcome,' she retorted. 'I came to see who was breaking in and entering.'

His eyebrows, which were several shades darker than his yellow-brown hair, went up in quizzical surprise and slowly, very slowly, he inspected her from the top of her head to the tip of her bare toes. By the time he had finished she was quivering with outrage. Acid blue now and extremely scornful, his glance swept up to her face.

'I did not break in,' he said softly and succinctly.

'You didn't knock at the door and wait to be invited in,' she countered. 'You slid open the window and came in that way. That amounts to breaking and entering.'

'The door was locked and I wasn't going to ignore a window which had been left invitingly open,' he retorted, and after giving her another scathing glance he turned away towards the kitchen

'What do you want?' she demanded, going after him and arriving in time to see him open the fridge door again.

'Right now, something to eat,' he replied coolly, surveying the contents of the fridge.

'But you have no right to . . . oh, I'm going to call

the police!' she exclaimed, and swinging round she made for the phone which was on one of the bookshelves built into the pine panelling of the living room.

For a big man, encumbered as he was by the oilskins, he moved fast with cat-like agility and the fingers of his right hand bit into her bare arm.

'Not so fast,' he said, and the soft purr of his voice sent tingles of alarm racing along her nerves. 'You'll only cause yourself a lot of embarrassment if you do that.'

'Don't you mean I'll cause you embarrassment?' she retorted angrily, pulling her arm free. 'You can't expect to break into and enter a house and then steal food and get away with it, you know. Look, I'll strike a bargain with you. If you'll leave the house now, go to your boat and not come back here, I'll promise not to call the police and I won't tell anyone you broke into the house to take food. You can go out this way.' She walked through into the hallway, switched on the light, opened the front door and pushed open the screen door. Damp fog drifted in, chilling her. 'Go on,' she ordered, as if speaking to a cat or a dog. 'Get out!'

He stood for a moment in the entrance to the living room, hands deep in the pockets of his oilskin jacket, his head tipped forward, watching her much as a lion might watch its prey before mauling it and again her nerves twanged. What would she do if he refused to go? Or if he touched her? He came towards her slowly, the oilskins rustling as he walked. He walked right up to her and she did her best not to back away from him, although she felt her knees shake.

But when his arm moved suddenly she cried out and raised her own arm as if to ward off a blow. He didn't touch her. Instead he took hold of the edge of the screen door, wrenched it out of her grasp and slammed it shut. Then he closed the heavy wooden front door with a crash which seemed to shake the frame and which echoed through the whole house. Knowing how lightly Heather slept, Margret was in no doubt that the child would wake up.

'Now why did you do that?' she complained, still trying to keep a calm composure. 'You'll have woken everyone up and lost your chance to get away.'

'That is if there's anyone to wake up,' he challenged. 'I doubt if there's anyone else in the house apart from you.'

'And if there isn't anyone else, what are you going to do?' she queried, returning the challenge, hoping that if she showed no fear of him he would back down and leave.

'What I came to do. I'll have something to eat and go to bed,' he replied easily. 'But not until I've found out why a strange woman is staying here, alone, in a house which belongs to my Aunt Marion.'

'Belongs to your aunt?' Margret thought her

laughter sounded just right, cool and mocking. 'Oh, come on, that's going a bit too far. This house belongs to a Mrs Lindley.'

'Exactly. Mrs Marion Lindley, who happens to be my aunt, widow of my uncle Earl Lindley. I'm Carl Lindley.'

Margret hoped he couldn't hear the sudden pounding of her heart. Wishing he wasn't standing so close to her, she folded her arms across her breast again, trying to ignore the way his cold bright glance shifted from her face to linger on the long line of her throat.

'Very clever,' she taunted. 'But you can't fool me like that. Carleton Lindley isn't in this country. He's in South America.'

'Who told you that?'

'My employer.'

'Who is?'

'Gregory Lindley. And he should know. He's Carleton Lindley's cousin.'

He considered her slowly and thoughtfully.

'So you work for Greg,' he murmured. 'To do what?'

'To look after his children and keep house for him . . . since his wife died last year,' she replied.

'Mmm. Aunt Marion told me Liza had died,' he said quietly, still watching her intently.

His knowledge of Greg's wife's first name, the easy way in which he referred to Mrs Lindley, who owned the house, as Aunt Marion, was beginning to make Margret realise she could have made a mistake about him, and she was racking her brains trying to think up a way to apologise to him without losing face when her attention was caught by a movement on the stairs and she looked in that direction. Heather and Jamie, both in pyjamas, were creeping down the stairs and in Jamie's right hand was a heavy old-fashioned pistol, one of a pair which decorated the wall of the upstairs landing with some rifles and old army sabres.

The man who claimed to be Carleton Lindley noticed the direction in which her glance had swerved and he looked that way too. His mouth widening into a grin that creased his lean cheeks, he walked over to the bottom of the stairs.

'Hi, kids,' he said in a friendly way.

They stopped coming and stood staring at him. Heather, who was just nine, was holding the six-year-old Jamie's left hand so tightly that he had difficulty in tugging it free.

'Let go! I'm not a baby,' he whispered fiercely.

His sister let go and Jamie was able to use his left hand to help his other hand to raise the pistol and point it directly at the man's head.

'If you hurt Margret,' the little boy lisped, 'I'll shoot you!'

'But I'm not going to hurt Margret, son,' said the man calmly. 'Nor you, nor your sister. I'm Carl Lindley and your father is my cousin.'

'How can you be him?' retorted Heather in her

high clear voice as she pushed past Jamie and came down the stairs. 'He's away in South America. I heard Daddy telling Margret.'

'I was in Peru, it's true,' said the man. 'But I'm here now, on vacation.'

'How did you get here?' asked Jamie.

'On a sailing boat. I borrowed it from a friend of mine and sailed here from Camden today.'

'Where's your boat now?' said Jamie. He had lowered the pistol and it was dangling from his small hand.

'Out there, in the strait, in front of the house.'

'Is he really Daddy's cousin?' Heather hissed at Margret.

'I don't know, and I've no way of telling,' Margret whispered back.

Heather turned to the man, her plain fair face wearing its most self-important expression.

'Do you have any form of identification?' she asked loftily.

'Would a driving licence do?' said the man, his mouth quirking humorously at one corner.

'Would it, Margret?' asked Heather, her self-confidence deserting her suddenly.

'I suppose so,' muttered Margret.

The man slipped a hand into a pocket of his oilskin jacket and took out a leather wallet. He flipped it open and showed it to Heather. Moving forward, Margret looked down at the plastic-covered licence. It showed quite clearly the name Carleton Lindley and an address in Philadelphia.

'It does have the right name,' Heather whispered.

'But how do we know it's really your licence?' Margret challenged, glancing up at the man. 'You could have stolen it.'

He swore then, one crisp ear-singeing word which showed no consideration for the children's tender years or Margret's sensitivity.

'What's with you?' he demanded, glaring at her. 'How do I know you're who you say you are? How do I know these are Greg's children and that you're employed by him to look after them? How do I know you're not some squatters who've moved into the house for the night because you knew no one was living here? Do you have any form of identification to show?'

They stared at him, all frozen temporarily by his show of icy anger. Then Jamie dropped the pistol and it bumped slowly down the stairs to land at the feet of the man. Quickly he picked it up. He opened the breach, inspected it and closed it. Turning, he looked down at the small white-faced boy who was staring up at him with wide dark eyes.

'Guess you're Greg's son, all right,' the man drawled. 'You sure look like him.' He squatted down in front of Jamie, oilskins rustling, so that his face was on a level with the little boy's, and smiled at him warmly. 'Do you know who used to own this pistol?' he asked.

Jamie shook his head from side to side so that his dark brown silky hair shimmered under the electric light.

'It used to belong to my great-grandfather who was also called Carleton Lindley. He fought in the Civil War and used this pistol,' explained the man, and twirled the unloaded pistol expertly in his hand like a gunfighter in a western movie. Jamie watched it in fascination.

'Did he shoot anyone with it?' asked Heather, her interest also caught.

'I guess he must have done,' said the man, standing up straight and pushing the pistol into a pocket of his oilskin. 'And if you're really the children of my cousin Greg, the man who used to own this gun was your great-great-grandfather.'

Jamie's dark eyes slid sideways to Heather and then moved to Margret appealingly, and she knew then the time had come for her to back down.

'Mr Lindley brought us to stay here two weeks ago,' she explained stiffly.

'Where is he now?' asked the man.

'He's in Chicago. He'll be back at the weekend.' She took a deep breath and drew herself up to her full height. Even so she had to look up at him. 'I'm sorry I doubted you. I wouldn't have done so if you'd arrived in a more conventional way, by daylight in a car.' She couldn't help having a dig at him and she could tell he had noticed and appreciated her sarcasm by the way his mouth quirked. 'But since you also have doubts about us I suggest you call your cousin on the phone now. He left a Chicago number for me to call if I had any problems.

It's in the front of the telephone directory.' She pointed to the book which lay on the shelf by the phone.

His glance followed her pointing finger, then returned along the curve of her bare arm up to her shoulder to her face. She lowered her arm quickly. He had a way of looking at her which made her feel very much aware of the thinness and scantiness of her nightgown, making her wish she had thought to pull on a dressing gown.

'*Bravo!*' Mockery purred in his voice. 'That took a lot of effort.' The slight smile tilted one corner of his mouth upwards and for the first time she noticed that the right corner of his mouth was paralysed and a scar caused it to have a permanent downward twist. 'It's never easy to climb down from a position once you've taken it,' he went on. 'I accept your apology and offer one of my own. If I'd known you were in the house I wouldn't have entered it unannounced at night.'

'But Mrs Lindley said Greg could use it. She said we could stay here.'

'Maybe she did. I haven't seen her since I returned from Peru. She's away in Europe at the moment and I haven't corresponded with Greg on a regular basis since he eloped with Liza.'

'They eloped?' Margret exclaimed.

'That's what it's called, I believe, when two people go away together and marry in secret,' he remarked dryly.

'Is it all right for us to stay here?' Heather asked anxiously, pulling at Margret's hand to get her attention.

'Sure you can stay,' said the man. 'As long as you don't mind having company for a few days.'

'Yours?' asked Jamie. He had to tip his head back a long way to look up at Carl Lindley.

'That's right.'

'Will you take me for a sail on your boat?' said Jamie.

'Maybe. If the weather is good.'

'Me, too!' demanded Heather, pushing in front of her brother.

'You too.' Carl looked across at Margret. 'And you,' he added softly. 'That is if you'd like to come with us.'

His intent blue stare was like a shock, sending shivers down her spine. How on earth could she stay in this house if he was going to be here? But then how could she leave with the children? Where could they go? As Greg had said they could all live here rent-free until he had managed to find a job. But that had been before Carl Lindley had turned up.

'As you say, it will depend on the weather,' she replied, coolly non-committal.

'I'm tired!' wailed Jamie suddenly, and yawned. 'I want to go back to bed.'

'Okay, you do that . . . er . . . what's your name?' asked Carl Lindley.

'He's Jamie and I'm Heather,' announced Hea-

ther, very self-important again. 'I know all about
you. Daddy told me he used to spend his summer
holidays with you at this house and you used to take
him sailing in your dinghy. Did you dig for clams
too?'

'We did.'

'That's what Jamie and I are going to do in the
morning while the tide is out.'

'So why don't you follow Jamie up to bed or you
won't be up early enough to catch those clams?' suggested Carl Lindley.

'All right.' Heather smiled at him suddenly and
sweetly. 'I'm glad you've come. What shall Jamie
and I call you?'

'Carl will do. See you tomorrow,' he said firmly.

Heather took the hint and hurried up the stairs.
Margret moved towards the stairs not wanting to
be alone with Carl any longer than necessary, but a
sudden thought struck her.

'I suppose you know which room you're going to
sleep in,' she said, turning to look at him.

He had taken off the oilskin jacket and was sitting
on a chair pulling off the yellow trousers that
covered his jeans. Without the jacket he was less
bulky, but his shoulders were still wide under a blue
and white Icelandic sweater and when he stood up
the heavy muscles of his thighs and legs shaped the
tough material of the jeans.

'The gable room at the front was always mine,' he
said.

'Oh. That's where I've been sleeping,' she exclaimed. 'And the children are in the room next to it.' He came towards her and she backed up the first stair. 'I could move out and into one of the other rooms if you want to sleep in the gable room,' she added hurriedly, not liking the glint in the blue eyes as they roved over her again.

'Or we could share it,' he suggested softly, putting one foot on the bottom stair and a hand on the banister so that she was forced to back up another stair.

'Mr Lindley, I don't know what sort of person you think I am just because I keep house for your cousin and look after his children,' she began haughtily.

'I think you're a very attractive person,' he said. 'And I fully appreciate why he chose to employ you. He must find you nice to have around the house. Do you share the gable room with him when he's here?'

'No, I do not!' she exclaimed furiously.

'Holding out for marriage to him first?' he drawled nastily.

'And what if I am?' she challenged, her chin up at a fighting angle. 'Is it any business of yours?'

His eyes narrowed as he considered her again and he smiled slowly, that twisted, strangely attractive smile which for some reason set her nerves tingling.

'I could make it my business,' he said enigmatically. 'Did you ever meet Greg's wife, Liza?'

'No.'

'Do you know how she died?'

'There was an accident, I believe. She fell and hit the back of her head and went into a coma. She lingered for months. It was a terribly trying time for him,' she added, her voice low with the sympathy she had felt for Greg during the period when Liza had hovered between life and death.

'I guess it was.' Carl's voice rasped oddly and she glanced at him curiously. His face was set in hard lines and he was staring beyond her as if he could see something he didn't like. 'Why has Greg come back to the States?' he asked, his glance swerving back to her. 'Do you know?'

'To attend interviews at various universities. He's hoping to get a professorship to lecture in psychology. He has his doctorate now, from the university where he taught in Britain.'

'I see.' Again he considered her with interest and again she felt an urge to turn and run up the stairs to her room and lock herself in it. 'How long have you been employed by him?' he drawled.

'Ever since. . . .' She broke off, wondering how much she should tell him about Greg's private life.

'Before or after Liza left him?' he queried.

'After. He advertised and I applied,' she said stiffly.

'Are you in love with him?' The abrupt question startled her and she turned on him.

'I don't have to answer that question,' she retorted. 'And . . . and . . . I don't like the way you're looking at me,' she blurted out suddenly and rather childishly, backing up the stair again.

His eyebrows tilted derisively, but he didn't follow her this time.

'Now that's a pity because you're good to look at, especially in that nightgown. In fact you seem to me to be the most unlikely person to find acting as nanny to two kids and housekeeper to someone like Greg who spends most of his time with his nose in a book,' he drawled. 'Okay, okay,' he added with a touch of weariness, half turning away from her as she backed nervously up the stairs again. 'I won't look at you any more.' He raked a hand through his hair. 'Like Jamie I'm tired too and I'd like to go to bed. But you don't have to move out of the gable room. I'll sleep in one of the other rooms.'

'The beds aren't made up. Would you like me to. . . .'

'No, I wouldn't like you to make up a bed for me,' he interrupted her coldly, turning to go down the stairs. 'I'll fix it myself. Goodnight, Miss . . .?' He drawled the word out suggestively.

'Randall,' Margret replied faintly, and hurried up the stairs, going while the going was good.

Once she was in bed she snuggled her head into the pillow and closed her eyes, but she couldn't go to sleep because she could hear Carl Lindley moving about the house. His unexpected arrival had disturbed her in more ways than one. After three weeks of pleasant tranquillity in this peaceful retreat on the coast of Maine she felt resentful because she would have to share the house with him.

She had loved the house as soon as she had seen it on a sparkling afternoon in the middle of July when the wind had been ruffling the blue water of the strait into tiny white-crested waves. With its cedar timbers weathered to a silvery grey, its neat white shutters framing every window and its pointed front gable, the house had seemed to her to possess a storybook quality. Hiding among overgrown wild roses and tall grasses, overhung by the gnarled branches of ancient apple trees, it had been the country cottage of her dreams; a place she had imagined often enough but had never expected to live in.

'Are you sure we can stay here?' she had asked Greg.

'Quite sure,' he had said. 'It belongs now to my Aunt Marion, widow of my uncle Earl. It came to him through inheritance from my grandfather. There've been Lindleys on the Point since the original grant of land was made in the seventeenth century by some king of England and the family lived here until they decided to move to Boston. For many years now it's been used only as a holiday residence.'

'Won't your aunt be coming here?'

'Not this summer.'

'What about her children? Don't they use it?'

'She doesn't have any children and I doubt if Carl will be coming, I hear he's in South America somewhere.'

'Carl?' she queried.

'My one and only cousin, son of uncle Earl's twin brother Edwin.'

Margret turned restlessly. Greg had been wrong and the cousin with whom he hadn't corresponded with on a regular basis since he had eloped with his wife Liza had turned up at the Point after all.

Greg and Liza must have been very much in love with each other to have eloped, she thought drowsily. Yet when Greg had talked to her about his marriage she hadn't received an impression of a loving and romantic relationship. In fact, it had been one continual battle and Liza had been a flighty, fretful woman who had resented being a mother and a wife and had eventually deserted Greg and the children to go and live with another man.

Margret fell asleep suddenly and awoke next morning when the alarm went off. Rolling over, she reached out and stopped the jangling noise. Then, flopping back against pillows, she stared at the window, trying to remember what she had planned to do that morning.

Go clamming, with Heather and Jamie—that was it. She frowned at the clock. By now Jamie was usually up and in this room, poking at her to make her get up. The house seemed very quiet. Only outside were there noises, the repetitive musical chant of the white-throated sparrow, the strident shouts of seagulls.

Was it possible the children had slept in? Or had

they gone out already to the beach? Sliding out of bed, Margret went over to the window. The fog was curling back in thick pearl-grey folds from the dark spruces that covered the island. On the smooth water directly in front of the house a sleek dark blue yacht seemed to preen itself like a bird admiring its own perfect reflection.

The sight of the yacht triggered off her memory and all that had happened during the night blazed into her mind, dispersing the last mists of sleep just as the sun was burning off the fog. She hadn't dreamed that a boat had anchored in the small rock-strewn harbour. It was there. But it was still possible she had dreamed the rest, wasn't it? It was still possible Carl Lindley hadn't come.

Flinging off her nightgown she dressed quickly in navy blue shorts and a red cotton shirt and thrust her feet into sandals. After brushing it she looped her long dark brown hair back from her face and twisted it into a tight knot at the nape of her neck. The style made her look older, hardening her face. But that was how she wanted to look, older and less pretty than usual, because if he was in the house she didn't want Carl Lindley looking at her the way he had looked at her last night. She didn't want him making guesses about her and coming up with the right answers.

Slipping her glasses on, she left the room and looked into the next bedroom. Both children were fast asleep. Now where would she find Carl Lindley?

The door of a bedroom at the back of the house was slightly open. Margret tiptoed along the landing towards it, pushed it open further and stepping forward peered into the room.

The room faced east and bright sunlight slanted in through the window, streaking the double bed and gleaming on the tousled golden-brown hair of the man who was lying on the bed, covered only by a single sheet. He was lying on his stomach with his head buried on his bare arms which were folded on the pillow.

Nothing imaginary or dreamlike about him, thought Margret ruefully, as she stepped back. A board creaked under her feet. The man on the bed turned his head quickly, raised it and looked right at her.

'I didn't mean to disturb you,' Margret said stiffly. 'I was just . . . well, I thought I might have dreamed that you came last night,' she admittted frankly.

He sat up and the sheet fell away from his shoulders and chest, revealing that he had been tanned to the colour of teak by a hot sun. As if mesmerised by the muscular symmetry of his body, Margret stared at him.

'No, it wasn't a dream,' he said with that faint, taunting, twisted smile. 'I'm really here. And you didn't wake me. I was awake already listening to the silence. I'd forgotten how quiet it can be here, in the morning.' His glance drifted over her lingering on the shape of her legs and she wished she hadn't worn shorts. 'You look more real too, by daylight,' he said, and then, with a smothered laugh, he covered his eyes with one hand. 'Sorry about that,' he added, still laughing. 'I'd forgotten—you don't like me to look at you. Are Heather and Jamie up yet?'

'No, not yet. I'm letting them sleep in because they were disturbed in the night,' she said coolly.

'You're going to let them miss the clams?' he exclaimed, dropping his hand to stare at her. 'That's hardly fair when they're looking forward to digging.'

'They'll be too tired, and when they're tired they're very cross,' she argued. 'Besides, I'm not sure how to dig for clams.'

'Then leave them to me,' he said. 'I'll get them up and I'll take them clamming. You can have the day off, I'm sure you deserve one.'

Seeing that he was going to fling back the sheet and get out of bed, and guessing that he slept in the nude, Margret turned and fled from the room. Down the stairs she ran, straight into the living room. There she stood for a moment looking at the oilskins where they were tossed casually on the floor and trying to calm herself. How could she possibly stay in this house while Carl Lindley was here, taking over, ordering her about as if she were his employee and not Greg's? But how could she leave until Greg came back? Her glance wandered on to the telephone and she went over to it. Quickly she dialled the number of the hotel in Chicago where

Greg had told her he would be staying. Since the phone was a party line she got an operator asking for the number of the phone she was using, then after a series of clicks she heard someone announcing that she was through to the hotel.

The telephone in the room where Greg was staying rang several times before he answered.

'Hello.' His voice was thick with sleep.

'It's Margret,' she said.

'You're calling early,' he said irritably.

'Something has happened,' she explained.

'To Heather, to Jamie or to you?' he demanded, his voice clearing suddenly as he became concerned.

'No, we're all right—at least we are so far. But last night a man broke into the house.'

'A burglar?' he gasped.

'I thought he was, but he said he was your cousin.'

'Carl?' Greg's voice fairly crackled with surprise. 'You're sure?'

'Well, he does have a driver's licence with his name on it and an address in Philadelphia. . . .'

'What does he look like?' Greg interrupted her.

'About six feet tall, pretty hefty, blondish-brown hair, blue eyes, has a scar at the right corner of his mouth.'

'That's Carl all right. He was with the Marines in the Vietnam war and was wounded in the face.' Greg chuckled. 'How like him to turn up unexpectedly in the middle of the night! He was always a cloak and dagger type. Where is he now?'

Margret looked round. Dressed in jeans and a crisp blue short-sleeved shirt, Carl was just coming into the living room with Jamie, who was holding his hand. Heather was right behind them. Ignoring Margret, they all trooped through to the kitchen.

'Would you like to speak to him?' she said into the mouthpiece.

'Not right now. It can wait until I come on Friday, if he's still there then.' Greg sounded strangely reluctant.

'Couldn't we leave here, go and stay somewhere else?' she asked.

'Where, for instance?' Again Greg seemed irritable.' I can't afford for you to stay anywhere else, not until I've got fixed up with a job. Why do you want to leave? I thought you liked Lindley's Point.'

'I do. But now that your cousin has come I. . . .'

'He hasn't been unpleasant, has he?' Greg put in quickly.

'In what way?'

'Has he suggested that you should leave?'

'No. He said we could stay as long as we don't mind having his company. But I do mind having his company, and I'm not sure if I can stay here if he's going to be here.'

There was a short silence in which she could hear Greg breathing even though he was miles and miles away.

'Has he said how long he's staying?' he asked at last.

'No. Greg, couldn't you come back before Friday?'

'I'll try. I'm leaving here later today and driving over to Maine to see some people at the university there I didn't see before. Look, Margret, try to hang on there, until I come.'

'All right,' she said, succumbing to the pleading in his voice, imagining how he looked. Dark straight hair falling forward over a high forehead, deep velvety brown eyes with a slightly puzzled expression in them, well-shaped lips curving into an endearing boyish smile, he was a grown-up version of Jamie.

'Thanks. I knew I could depend on you.' He sounded relieved. 'And don't let Carl upset you. Try to be diplomatic.'

'I'll do my best.'

'Good. Wish me luck now, with the interviews.'

'Good luck. We'll look forward to seeing you.'

Margret put the receiver down and for a moment stood staring out of the window at the sun-bright water of the strait. It had been a waste of time and money calling Greg, and she should have known it would be. Be diplomatic, that was the only advice he could give her. But it wasn't going to be easy for her to be diplomatic towards Carl Lindley, because there was something about him that put her on the defensive. She was frightened of him, but she couldn't think why.

In the kitchen Heather was setting the table while Jamie stood beside Carl, who was at the cooker tipping the frying pan this way and that to melt fat.

'Carl is making blueberry pancakes for us,' lisped Jamie.

'But you don't like blueberry pancakes. You wouldn't eat the ones I made yesterday for breakfast and I had to throw them out,' said Margret, picking up the kettle and taking it to the sink.

'We do like them. We just didn't like yours,' Heather explained. 'Carl's will be better. He knows how to make them because he learned from his Aunt Marion.'

'Well!' Margret could think of nothing else to say as she felt resentment simmer within her because the children had taken so little time to transfer their loyalty from herself to Carl. Talk about blood being thicker than water! As she plugged in the kettle she gave Carl an irritated glance and encountered his mocking sideways glance at her.

'Don't take it to heart,' he said with his twisted smile. 'You can have your job as cook back any time. Is the water for coffee?'

'I don't drink coffee for breakfast,' she retorted. 'I prefer tea.'

'You would,' he countered, and scooped a perfectly round golden pancake from the pan to lay it with the other pancakes he had cooked on a plate being kept warm on top of the cooker.

'After breakfast Carl is coming with us to show us

how to dig for clams,' said Heather, who was apparently in one of her organising moods. 'You needn't come, Margret, he'll look after us.'

'And after we've dug for clams we're going on his boat,' said Jamie.

'If it isn't too windy,' said Margret weakly.

'The weather forecast is good for the next few days,' Carl added. 'Maybe we should go for a cruise among the islands.'

'Ooh, yes! Yes, please!' Heather cried, jumping up and down. 'I'd like that.'

'I don't know anything about sailing,' said Margret stiffly. She had a strong feeling that the children were getting quite beyond her control.

'You can learn,' said Carl crisply. 'Now why don't you three sit down and start on the pancakes. Time is moving along and the tide won't stay out forever.'

For once the children did as they were told immediately. They didn't even squabble about places at the table, and as Margret poured fresh orange juice for them she felt resentment boiling up inside her again because Carl had taken over so easily.

By the time she had made the tea and had taken her place at the table he had finished making pancakes and was sitting at the table.

'I could make you some instant coffee,' she offered diffidently, remembering Greg's warnings to her to be diplomatic.

'Don't bother. Tea will do. Black and without sugar,' he said curtly.

'Your pancakes are scrumptious,' Heather said.

The girl certainly knew how to flatter in the right places, thought Margret irritably. 'I hope you're going to stay with us for a long time and make them every day, Carl.'

'Thanks for the compliment,' he replied smoothly. 'Have you and Jamie finished?'

'Yes, thanks,' said Heather, while Jamie nodded.

'Then go and get the buckets and the other things you'll need for digging clams and go down to the shore. I'll be with you in a few minutes when I've finished eating,' said Carl. 'And don't forget to put your boots on. We don't want sneakers in the mud, and we don't want mud in the house. Okay?'

'Okay,' chorussed the children, and went out to the back porch where their billy boots were kept.

Margret began to rise to her feet, even though she hadn't finished eating.

'I'd better go and help them,' she muttered.

'Finish your meal first, or I'll be thinking you don't like my pancakes,' said Carl. 'They can put their boots on without your help. Anyway, I want to have a few words with you.'

'I really think I'd better go,' she said stubbornly.

'Sit down!' He spoke sharply and for a moment she glared furiously at him, intending to defy him. Then she remembered again about being diplomatic and sank into her chair and picked up her fork. 'Were you talking to Greg, just now, on the phone?' he asked.

'Yes.' She scooped up some light fluffy pancake dotted with blueberries.

'Why did you call him?'

'To tell him you'd come.' She put the pancake in her mouth. It was smooth and seemed to melt on her tongue.

'Checking up on me, huh?' he drawled. 'Making sure I'm Carl Lindley, I guess. You know you could have done that by asking Nelson or Millie White. They would identify me. Did Greg tell you when he's coming back?'

'He hopes to be here on Friday.'

'So we have three days. That isn't very long.'

'For what?' she asked, looking up warily. His brawny forearms, glistening with golden hairs, were resting on the table and he was leaning forward, looking at her with narrowed speculative eyes.

'For you and me to get to know each other better,' he said.

'I don't want to know you better.'

'Okay.' He shrugged. 'For me to get to know you better, then.' His glance roved over her and he frowned. 'What the hell have you done with your hair?' he growled.

'I always do it this way.'

'I don't like it.'

'Don't you? But I don't arrange my hair to please you. I do it the way I want to please myself,' she retorted sweetly.

Behind her the screen door of the porch clanged shut and she heard Heather's and Jamie's voices as they passed by the open window of the kitchen on their way to the shore.

'Are you really going clamming with them?' she asked, rising to her feet again. 'If not, I'll go. Jamie needs watching. He can't swim yet.'

'I'm going.' Carl also stood up and moved round the table towards her. 'But there's just one more thing that puzzles me.' He stopped in front of her and sensing a threat in his stealthy catlike movements Margret tensed, ready to move away. But he was too quick for her. He reached out and whipped the glasses from her nose.

'Give them back to me!' she demanded angrily.

'Not yet.' He lifted them beyond her reach and tilting his head to one side studied her face. 'The hair-do and these glasses make you look a hell of a lot older than you looked last night in your nightie,' he scoffed. He lowered the glasses and stared at them curiously. 'Is that why you wear them? Do you want to look older than you are?'

'Please give them back,' she said. 'I can't see well without them.'

'You could see all right last night,' he remarked. 'Haven't you ever thought of wearing contact lenses?' He raised the glasses to his eyes and peered at her through them.

'No, I haven't,' she retorted through set teeth. He lowered the glasses again and studied her face once more, his mouth slanting in its twisted smile.

'Without them I'd put you at twenty-four,' he commented. 'With your hair loose, you look even younger. How close am I?'

He had guessed her age accurately, but she wasn't going to let him have the satisfaction of knowing he was right.

'I'm thirty,' she said, looking him right in the eyes.

'Ah, come on!' he jeered.

'Now can I have my glasses, please?' She held out her hand. He didn't give them to her.

'Has Greg ever seen you without them?' he asked.

'No. At least I don't think so.'

'Or with your hair loose?'

'I really don't see the point of this . . . this inquisition,' she retorted. 'Please give me the glasses. I need them.'

'But they're made of clear glass,' he argued. 'And they wouldn't help anyone to see any farther or to read either. They're stage props, nothing more, the sort an actress might wear for a part in a play.'

'Please give them to me,' she replied woodenly.

'Later,' he replied tauntingly. 'Perhaps when I go away from here.' To her secret dismay he folded the glasses and slid them into the breast pocket of his shirt. 'And now for the hair,' he said, and stepped towards her.

'Don't you dare touch it!' she flared, backing away from him. 'I . . . I'll scream if you do!'

'How very unoriginal of you, Miss Randall,' he mocked, still advancing towards her. 'If you do scream no one will hear you except me.'

'Heather and Jamie might. I can scream very loudly.'

'So they might,' he agreed, still coming. She backed into the sink unit and he leaned over her so that she could feel the warmth of his body. 'But go right ahead, scream if you want to. I know of a good way to silence you,' he whispered.

Again he moved quickly, his hand, like a big golden paw, reaching for the knot at the nape of her neck. Taking a deep breath, Margret opened her mouth to scream and immediately he bent his head and covered her lips with his own.

Vainly she struggled to free herself from that silencing kiss, twisting her head, pushing at him with her hands, even kicking at his shins, but nothing she did seemed to have any effect, and as her hair was loosened to fall about her face and shoulders his arms went around her.

Held closely against him, her soft breasts crushed by the hardness of his chest, Margret willed herself to endure and not respond as his kiss became deeper and more searching. But it was hard to resist the seductive movements of his lips against hers and she had to admit she liked the feel of his strong arms about her shoulders. And the scent of his suntanned, sea-salted skin was rising to her head like an inhaled drug, causing it to spin. Any moment now she would give in to the desire which was swelling within her; a desire to reach up and fondle his thick mane of hair, to part her lips invitingly beneath his, to meet passion with passion.

'Carl, aren't you coming with us?' Heather's clear childish voice called from the back porch. It was like a splash of cold water, cooling them instantly and bringing them back to sanity. Carl raised his head, his arms fell to his sides and he stepped back, but his eyes, a dark burning blue now, still held Margret's, which were wide and bewildered above the hand which she had pressed against her throbbing lips.

'I'll be with you in a minute, Heather,' he called back, and the porch door clanged shut again. There was a second of breathless silence as he and Margret continued to stare at each other. Then he smiled mockingly.

'That was interesting,' he drawled, the expression in his eyes veiled suddenly by the thick bronze-coloured lashes. 'You're not as frozen as you'd have everyone believe you are. We must try it again some time. See you later!'

CHAPTER TWO

LEFT alone in the house, Margret used the energy resulting from her exploding irritation, not only with Carl Lindley but also with herself, to do some necessary housework while the children were out of the way and, by the time she had finished changing beds and making them, had put a load of sheets and clothes in the washing machine and had vacuumed the floors and dusted the furniture, she had simmered down. No longer did she want to pack her cases and walk out of the Lindleys' house never to return. She would stay.

She would stay because Greg had asked to stay. No matter what Carl Lindley did or said to her she would 'hang on' for the next few days because ... well, because she had no choice really, she thought with a wry grimace as she put the vacuum cleaner away. To leave either with the children or without them she would have to have money, and at the moment she had very little since Greg had not paid her recently and she had used all that he had given her for housekeeping.

Anyway, pride forbade that she should let herself be stampeded away just because a tough ex-Marine had seen through her disguise and had kissed her. But she frowned anxiously as she made herself a drink of iced tea and carried it through to the living room to sit on a window seat and sip it, while she looked out at the view of the sun-dazzled water and the dark spruce-covered island beyond it. Somehow she had to get her glasses back from Carl before Greg returned.

She wouldn't have disguised herself if she hadn't been so desperate for a job. Trained to be an actress, she had worked for nearly two years on the stage with various touring companies, cast always in minor roles and often having to help out with costumes and stage management. Sometimes to supplement her meagre wages she had done photographic modelling, some film crowd and television work and had worked as a demonstrator at exhibitions. She had also served in coffee bars and had sold tickets in a cinema.

Then at last, eighteen months ago her big chance had come. She had been auditioned for a role in the London production of a new play and had been chosen. After weeks of gruelling rehearsals the play had opened and after a week of controversy had been closed. Once again Margret had been out of work, and it had been then that she had taken stock of her situation, indulging in some pretty sharp self-analysis and coming to the reluctant conclusion that she was never going to be a success as an actress and wasn't even able to keep herself by acting.

She had applied for the first position she had seen advertised in a London paper which had not required any sort of special training.

'Companion for two young children required. Must be willing to live in and keep house also. Quiet, well-educated woman in thirties or forties would suit.'

A telephone number had been provided and she had called it immediately. It had turned out to be the number of an agency which catered mostly to foreign families or to British families living abroad who wanted someone to look after children. She had been interviewed first by a sharp-eyed middle-aged woman, who had been one of the partners in the agency.

'You seem capable enough, Miss Randall,' the woman had said. 'And you speak very well—the stage training, I suppose. What experience have you had with children?'

'I have two young half-brothers and I've often looked after them for my stepmother.'

'And what about general household management? Do you like that sort of thing? Shopping for food, budgeting, cleaning cooking and so on?'

'I can do it. I kept house for a short time when I was younger, until my father married again,' Margret had answered, but her spirits had slowly been sinking as she had realised that the job she had applied for did warrant some sort of special training after all. 'Mrs Kerridge, I'm really desperate for a job,' she had pleaded urgently. 'I hope you'll put my name forward for this one.'

Mrs Kerridge had looked her over with critical eyes and then had looked down at the list of specifications for the position which lay on the desk in front of her.

'How old are you, Miss Randall?' she had asked.

'Twenty-two, nearly twenty-three.'

'You don't seem to have read the advertisement very well,' Mrs Kerridge said dryly. 'It does say a woman in her thirties or forties. However, this is the fourth week we've advertised this particular position and you're the only person who has shown any keenness. Dr Lindley is an American who is at present teaching in the sociological department of one of our universities. Unfortunately his wife has deserted him and the children. He needs someone to look after the children, but since there's the possibility of his wife returning he can't say the job will be a permanent one, and so many of the older women, who are experienced and trained to do this sort of job, require permanency.' Mrs Kerridge had paused, frowning thoughtfully. 'I think I'm going to take a chance on you,' she said at last, slowly, her rather severe face softening into a smile. 'I'll tell Dr Lindley about you and make an appointment for you to meet him. But it would help if you could try to look not so young, and not so pretty.'

The appointment had been made and on the following Friday a slim woman with dark brown hair drawn back tightly into a knot at the nape of her neck, who was wearing a nondescript brown tweed suit and a silky beige blouse and who had rather large heavily rimmed glasses covering her lovely amber-coloured, black-fringed eyes, had travelled down to the university town of Seaham, on the south coast, and had presented herself at the small suburban house where Gregory Lindley had lived.

It hadn't taken Margret long to realise that the handsome American with the unhappy dark eyes and diffident charming smile had been just as desperate to find someone to look after his children while their mother was absent as she had been to get a job, and it had taken only half an hour for them to come to an agreement about working conditions and wages. He hadn't seem to notice her appearance and he had never asked how old she was. At the time she had decided his lack of interest was good. It had meant that her disguise had been successful, but now she wondered whether he had been easy to deceive or whether he had been too relieved to find someone suitable to bother to ask questions and examine her more closely.

She had been with the family for two months when the news came that Liza Lindley had been injured in a car accident, and she knew that Greg had been glad she had been there during that time when he had been so anxious. Four weary months later Liza had died, and Margret's job as childminder and housekeeper had become a permanent one. She had been happy to continue with it because, by then, she had become completely captivated by Heather and Jamie, recognising their need for someone like herself to provide stability in their lives, knowing that their mother had been capricious and wilful and that Greg, although charming and gentle, was a typical professor, very good at the research in which he was involved, an excellent teacher, but extremely vague and impractical when it came to coping with the mundane, everyday happenings of life.

Her simple disguise hadn't been difficult to maintain over the months and neither of the children seemed to notice that she looked different if they saw her without her glasses or with her hair loose, and it was because they made no comment that she had grown careless while they had been at Lindley's Point and while Greg was away.

But now she was worried. Even if she had the glasses by the time Greg returned she had no doubts Carl Lindley would tell his cousin that he suspected she had practised deceit in order to get a job. And Greg would be hurt when he knew, she was sure of that. He might even think of sacking her.

Margret finished her drink and leaving the living room went out through the front door on to the wide sun-deck. The tide was creeping in slowly, sliding in smooth shining ripples over gleaming, ochre-coloured mud. All the fog had gone and beyond Hog's Island she could see other islands, floating like gold-rimmed emeralds on a sea of turquoise. In the small harbour the dark blue boat was swinging round, its stainless steel fittings glittering in the bright hot sunshine. As usual it was very quiet, except for the occasional cry of a gull. Too quiet, for there should be the sound of Heather's and Jamie's voices as they dug for clams.

Shading her eyes, Margret looked along the shore in both directions but could see neither the children nor the tall figure of a man. Of course, the tide had covered the clamming areas by now, so they must have stopped digging. Had they gone out to the boat? She jumped down off the wooden deck on to grass that sloped down to the shore. The rubber dinghy in which Carl had come ashore was still there, pulled up clear of the clumps of brown rock-weed which marked the high tide level, cradled among some rocks, its oars stowed neatly, its painter tied round a convenient single upright rock.

Where had they gone? Wishing suddenly that she had never let the two children out of her sight, Margret walked back to the narrow lane that led from the house up to the road, twisting her hair into its tight knot as she went. Five minutes later, breathless with hurrying in the heat of the day, she arrived at the old farmhouse where Nelson and Millie White lived.

Built in what she knew now to be traditional New England style from wood, its huge barn connected to it by a long passage, the house was located on a green knoll of land with magnificent views of the long stretch of water known as The Reach. It was painted white and in its front garden crimson and purple dahlias, orange and yellow nasturtiums, huge golden brown-eyed sunflowers and elegant pink hollyhocks flowered in unkempt profusion, creating brilliant splashes of colour. There was no one on the shady verandah and no one came to the front door when she knocked, so she went round the side of the house, past a pile of slatted lobster traps and brightly painted trap buoys to the wide open field at the back of the house. In the midst of rows of cabbages, potatoes, corn and other vegetables she spotted Millie, squatting down, apparently gathering something.

Short and plump, wearing an old cotton sun-hat and a sleeveless cotton dress, Millie looked round when she heard Margret call her name and stood up.

'My soul, you sure look different without those peepers you usually wear,' she drawled. 'I didn't recognise you for a second. Did you break them?'

'I . . . er . . . no.' Margret shaded her eyes selfconsciously with one hand. 'Have you seen Heather and Jamie, by any chance?'

'I sure have.' Millie bent and picked up the basket of peas she had gathered and began to walk towards the house. 'They were here about a half hour ago, with Carl. Land sakes, was I surprised to see him! He says you thought he was a burglar last night.' Millie chuckled heartily. 'Wouldn't do him any harm to have someone stand up to him, the way he says you did. He's a sight too fond of riding roughshod.'

'Where are they now?' asked Margret.

'Nelson has taken them in the truck to Roskeag Harbour to sell the clams they dug this morning.'

'Sell them?'

'Sure. Clams are fetching twenty-two dollars a bushel this summer.'

'But Heather and Jamie can't have dug a bushel,' exclaimed Margret as they came round the house to the front verandah.

'Not on their own, no,' said Millie as she clumped up the wooden steps. 'But they had help this morning, good help too. Carl was always a great clam digger. Always sharp when it came to selling them too. I wouldn't be surprised if those kids don't come back from Roskeag with a fistful of dollars each.'

'He shouldn't have taken Heather and Jamie to sell them,' Margret objected. 'I don't think Greg . . . their father would approve.'

'Well, what do you expect them to do with all those clams except sell them?' retorted Millie. 'No, I reckon Carl had the right idea encouraging them to sell the fruits of their labours. They have to learn some time. They're not going to make it in this world if they don't.'

'I still think Greg wouldn't approve of such young children making money from the fruits of their labours,' Margret argued mildly. It wasn't the first time she had heard Millie's strong puritanical beliefs in the virtues of hard work and free enterprise.

'Guess you're right, he wouldn't,' retorted Millie,

setting down the basket of peas and plonking herself in an old rocking chair. 'He was always the dreamer and Carl was always the worker. Take the weight off your feet while you can,' she invited, waving a hand to another rocking chair. 'Whew, it's hot today! Must be about ninety degrees. Reckon Carl has brought some good weather with him.'

'How long have you known him?' Margret asked as she sat cautiously on the edge of the other rocker, the seat of which looked as if it might collapse any minute, it was so worn through.

'Most of his life, ever since his uncle brought him here for a summer vacation. Earl and Marion Lindley didn't have any kids of their own and when Carl's parents were both killed in an accident they adopted Carl and brought him up as their own son. My soul, how time flies! He came here for the first time when he was two, almost thirty-two years ago. I was about ten, then, and now I'm pushing forty-four and about to be a grandmother for the second time and he isn't even married yet. Time he stopped roving and settled down.'

'How does he earn his living?' asked Margret.

'He's an engineer of some sort. Works for one of those big construction companies that build bridges and dams. That's what he's been doing out there in Peru, he was telling me. Says he's going back out there to finish the job.' Millie gave Margret one of her sharp inquisitive glances. 'Any chance of Greg coming back while Carl is here?'

'He should be back Friday.'

'You'll have told Carl about the death of Greg's wife, I guess,' Millie went on probingly. 'How did he take it?'

'He knew about it already.'

'He brought her to Lindley's Point, you know. She was a nurse in the hospital where they stitched him up after he was wounded.' Millie mopped at her forehead. 'He seemed to be real fond of her. Reckon it must have shook him up some when she went off with Greg. Did you ever meet her?'

'No.' Margret moved uneasily. She didn't want to get involved in a discussion about her employer's dead wife with Millie. 'How long do you think they'll be at Roskeag?'

'God knows. It'll depend on Nelson and how long he stands around there gossiping. Why don't you make the most of having some time to yourself and do some sunbathing?'

'I think I will.'

Back at Lindley's Point Margret changed into a black bikini and taking a book with her went to lie on one of the loungers on the sun-deck. She smoothed sun-tan lotion on her skin and for a while tried to read, but the mystery failed to hold her. She was much more interested in pondering on what Millie had told her about Carl and Liza.

Feeling her face, chest and the front of her legs and arms growing hot, she lowered the back of the lounger and turning on to her stomach pillowed her head on her arms. So Carl had been 'real fond' of Liza, had he? Margret smiled to herself as she recalled Millie's description of Carl's feelings for the woman. Fondness for a person was not something she could associate with the rugged tough guy who had invaded the peace of Lindley's Point last night. When he loved anyone—*if* he ever loved anyone— it would be violently and wholeheartedly, and she couldn't imagine he would let go easily anyone he loved, having felt the strength of his arms about her. She couldn't imagine any woman wanting to escape from a man who held her like that, either.

The warmth of the sun combined with the soft shushing sound of the waves on the shore lulled her gradually into a doze from which she woke with a start when she felt something crawling down her spine. She opened her eyes but didn't move, wondering whether she had imagined the tickling sensation. Then it happened again, and she recognised that someone was trailing a fingertip delicately down her bare back.

Thinking it was Jamie because he often liked to tease her, she reached round a hand to catch at his hand, but instead of closing round the slim smooth wrist of a little boy, her fingers encountered the thick sinewy hair-furred forearm of a man. At once she let go and lunging up on an elbow turned. Carl was sitting on another lounger, his elbows on his knees, his chin cupped in his hands, and was watching her with amused blue eyes.

'Where are Heather and Jamie?' Margret demanded, annoyed because he had been there looking at her while she had dozed and had dared to touch her again.

'Down on the shore,' he replied casually. But there was nothing casual about the way he was looking at her.

'You should have come and asked me if you could take them to Roskeag to sell clams,' she said sharply, determined to put up barriers between herself and him because this third meeting with him was having strange effects on her. Or was she suffering from too much sun? Her senses were behaving most unusually and she was experiencing a crazy, heady desire to show him she was glad to see him again. She wanted to reach out and touch him, even invite him to kiss her.

'And risk having you say no?' he queried. He shook his head so that the thick pelt of his blond-streaked hair shimmered in the sunlight, but his intent gaze never left her eyes. 'That isn't the way I operate,' he added softly, leaning towards her. He placed his hands on the cushion of the lounger on which she was sitting, one on either side of her bare thighs, almost touching them. 'Once I've decided what I want to do I do it,' he murmured.

'So I'd noticed,' she remarked shakily, putting her arms behind her and leaning back on them, away from him as far as she could go because there was temptation in his lips and eyes. 'But you seem to have forgotten that Heather and Jamie are my responsibility while their father is away. I have to know where they are and know who they're with.'

'Don't you trust me?' he asked ambiguously, leaning closer.

'No, I don't,' she whispered, unable now to stop looking at his mouth. His hands slid sideways and curved along her thighs and she shivered suddenly with excitement.

'It's been a long time since I met someone like you,' he said, the deep murmur of his voice hardly louder than the murmur of the waves. 'And I'm not going to restrain another urge to kiss you again.'

'No!' she gasped weakly as his hands crept up to her bare waist and he drew her towards him. 'I wish you'd leave me alone,' she added more strongly, tilting her head back, and at once he kissed her, lightly and tantalisingly.

It was a torment of a kiss, promising much but giving nothing, making her feel as if something had been stolen from her, so that she raised her hand and slapped him lightly on his cheek as he raised his head, only to have her hand caught and enfolded in his warm grasp.

'How . . . how dare you!' she muttered, unable to think of anything else to say, and his delighted laughter infuriated her. Twisting her hand free of his, she managed to get to her feet and back away from him. 'If you think that was funny I think you have a very warped sense of humour!' she flared.

'I was laughing at what you said,' he retorted, rising to his feet. *'How dare you!'* He mimicked her accent and laughed again. 'I didn't believe women said things like that any more. It sounded like a line from a Victorian novel or play, like that other line you used when you said you'd scream if I touched you.' His glance raked her scantily clad body. 'Neither are in keeping with the way you look, and you don't mean either of them.'

'Yes, I do,' she replied, stepping round the back of one of the loungers so that it was a real barrier between them. 'I don't like men who make passes at women they've only just met, and I wish you hadn't come here. If . . . if . . . I hadn't promised Greg I'd stay here and wait until he comes back I'd have left this morning and taken the children with me rather than stay in the same house as you!'

In the curious little silence that followed she was aware of the glitter of sunlight on the water, of the shrill voices of the children and the hum of a car's engine as the vehicle approached the house down the narrow lane.

'I had no idea I'd made such a big impression on you,' Carl drawled mockingly, then looked away from her at the car which was turning from the lane on to the grass beside the house. It stopped, its engine was turned off, both front doors swung open and a man and a woman got out.

'I was wondering how long it would be before Laura dropped in to see who was here,' Carl said dryly. He turned back to Margret, his eyes glinting wickedly. 'Again getting to know you has to be postponed, but I'll look forward to our next encounter. I have a feeling it will be even more interesting.'

He strode away along the deck, calling out a greeting to the couple by the car. The woman hurried towards him, reaching out both arms, and they embraced. Feeling shaky and very confused, Margret went to the edge of the deck and jumped down on to the grass and made her way towards Heather and Jamie, who were digging channels in the sand for the encroaching tide to fill.

'It's past lunch time,' she said. 'Are you coming to the house to have a sandwich and some milk?'

'We've had our lunch,' replied Heather. 'We had it with Carl at the lunch counter in Roskeag General Store.'

'What did you have?' Margret asked. Greg was very particular about the children's diet and since Heather had a liking for fried foods and sweet things she had to be watched carefully.

'Hot dogs,' Heather's underbrowed look was defiant, 'and Coke.'

'But you know your father doesn't like you to have either,' Margret objected with a touch of exasperation. 'Oh, I knew I shouldn't have let you out of my sight! And you shouldn't have gone to Roskeag without telling me first. You must always come and ask my permission before you go anywhere with a stranger.'

'Carl isn't a stranger,' argued Jamie. 'He's our cousin.' Getting to his feet, he came over to her and pushed a muddy, gritty hand into hers and looked up at her appealingly. 'Don't be angry with us, Margret,' he lisped. 'We had a lot of fun with Carl and we got sixteen dollars for our clams, that's eight dollars for me and eight dollars for Heather.'

Margret stared down at him and then at Heather, a sense of defeat washing over her. It was very obvious that in the few hours he had been in their lives Carl had managed to conquer them completely. They would never listen to anything she might say against him now, she thought ruefully, but she had to make one last try.

'And that's another thing your father wouldn't approve of,' she began, but Carl's voice interrupted her, drawing their attention away from her.

'Heather, Jamie, come over here. Someone wants to meet you,' he called.

They obeyed him instantly, racing across the grass to jump up on the sun-deck, responding to his crisp command much more easily than they ever did to her own pleadings or their own father's gentle psychologically-balanced requests. Carl was like a magician, Margret thought fancifully, as she followed the children, and even she was beginning to succumb to his rough magic.

She climbed on to the deck just in time to hear Carl introducing the children to the woman, Laura Spencer and the young man, who was Brett Spencer.

'Isn't Greg here?' asked Laura, looking round. Tall and well-built, she was wearing white pants and an olive green sleeveless shirt. Her bright hair was naturally wavy but not naturally blonde, Margret decided. Unaware of her own attractions, shapely tanned legs and figure shown off to advantage by the skimpy bikini, silky dark hair flowing loosely about her shoulders and caressing her peach-gold cheeks, she moved forward to stand behind Heather.

'No, but he's coming on Friday,' said Carl. 'And this is Margret Randall, who looks after the kids and keeps house for Greg.'

Laura gave Margret an icy glance from wide-spaced grey eyes, nodded frigidly, then turned her back deliberately and putting a hand on Carl's arm turned him away with her so she could say something quietly to him.

Her cheeks flaming because she had been snubbed by the woman, Margret turned blindly to stalk away into the house, only to find Brett Spencer barring her way, his hand stretched out.

'Nice to meet you,' he said. About her own age, he was long and lean, dressed in typical student uniform of jeans and a sweat shirt on which the name of his university had been printed, and his longish brown hair was confined by an embroidered head-band. His grin was friendly and his grey eyes twinkled warmly as their glance drifted over her admiringly. 'How long have you been here?' he asked after they had shaken hands.

'About three weeks.'

'I wish I'd known you were here. I'd have come calling on you. There aren't too many people like you staying around here this summer. Apart from the Whites we're the nearest neighbours . . . that is when we're here. Our place is about a mile along the shore, towards Roskeag, and, like the Lindleys, our family has always come here for the summer months. Laura and Jack, my elder brother, used to go about with Carl and Greg. I belong to a younger age group.'

'I'm pleased to meet you,' said Margret, making an effort to be pleasant although she was still smarting from Laura's deliberate snub. 'Can I get you a drink? We have lemonade, iced tea . . . or beer, if you prefer it.'

Carl and Brett opted for beer, Laura said she would have iced tea and the children chose lemonade. Glad to escape indoors, Margret ran upstairs and changed into a simple cotton dress that covered her from neck to calf, leaving only her arms bare. She hadn't liked the way Laura Spencer had looked her up and down when she had been wearing the bikini. Binding up her hair again into its tight knot, wishing she had her disguising glasses and wondering anxiously what Carl had done with them, she hurried downstairs and reached the hall just as Brett walked in.

'I thought I'd give you a hand with the drinks,

open beer cans or something,' he said in his friendly way. 'Also I can't stand it when Laura is being in-sincere.' He grinned widely when Margret gave him a surprised enquiring glance. 'Right now she's saying how sorry she is to hear about Liza's death,' he added.

'And that's being insincere?' said Margret.

'I happen to know how much she disliked Liza,' he drawled.

Although she longed to know why the cool, self-assured Laura had disliked Greg's wife Margaret didn't say anything. She went through to the kit-chen and Brett followed her, to lean against the table while she took the beer and lemonade from the fridge.

'She didn't exactly take a liking to you, either, did she?' Brett went on. 'You must have noticed how she snubbed you when you were introduced. She was hoping to find either Greg or Carl here alone and it really shook her when you appeared. It was more or less a repeat performance of a little scene which was enacted in the same place ten years ago when Carl came here to convalesce after he'd been wounded in Vietnam and he brought his latest girl-friend with him, a nurse called Liza.'

'But surely your sister doesn't believe there's anything between Carl and me?' exclaimed Mar-gret, whirling round to face him. 'I've only just met him. He didn't come until last night.'

'That won't change Laura's way of thinking. She

knows what a fast operator he is. And she's always been possessive about Carl and Greg. She's known both of them ever since they were all kids, vacationing here together. She used to write Carl regularly when he was in Vietnam. She went to college and university with Greg ... they're both in the same line, educational psychology. Her trouble has been not being able to make up her mind which of them she likes best, so she lost out, ten years ago, to Liza.'

'Liza married only one of them,' Margret reminded him with a touch of dryness as she spooned instant tea into a tall glass.

'Granted. But after she went away with Greg, Carl cleared out, went abroad, presumably to lick his wounds, much to my sister's chagrin.' Brett gave a chuckle of laughter. 'Oh, I tell you, Margret, it was a real tangle here that summer with both Carl and Greg hot for Liza and Laura left out in the cold. It was just like the tangle in *A Midsummer Night's Dream*. Are you familiar with Shakespeare's play? I happen to be an English Literature buff myself and am in the process of working for my Master's degree.'

'Yes, I know the play,' answered Margret, who could quote at length from it, having once played the part of Titania in a school production.

'I'm going to see it tonight, at an open-air theatre. Like to come with me?' said Brett.

'There's a theatre near here?'

'At Camden . . . which is about sixty miles away. It operates only in the summer, but puts on some pretty good productions.'

'I'd love to go,' Margaret said fervently, her eyes sparkling. 'But how can I? Someone has to stay with Heather and Jamie.'

'I'll ask Laura to keep an eye on them for you, if you like.' Brett's eyes twinkled again with warm humour. 'It would give her a chance to be alone with Carl.'

And would give me a chance to escape from him for a while, thought Margret, as she finished pouring lemonade.

'What do you say?' asked Brett, as he tore tops off the beer cans and began to pour the liquid into glasses. 'Would you like me to suggest it when we take the drinks out?'

'I'm not sure. I don't really like leaving them. Yet it's ages since I was in a theatre and saw a play.'

'Look at it this way. It isn't as if you'd be leaving them with someone strange. Laura knows Greg well and he knows her, so I don't think he would have any objection if he knew,' argued Brett.

'All right. You can ask her,' said Margret.

Much to her surprise Laura's attitude towards her changed miraculously when Brett announced casually that he would like to take Margret to the theatre that evening, but there was the problem of finding someone to stay with Heather and Jamie.

'No problem,' Laura spoke up with a smile. 'I'll

be glad to have them. They can come over to our place for dinner. You come too, Carl. I know Mother would love to see you again and to meet Greg's children. Why don't we walk over there soon, along the shore, like we used to do? These two youngsters . . .' she waved a hand in the direction of Margret and Brett, like an indulgent aunt giving them permission to go out, 'can leave as soon as they like. It's a long drive to Camden.'

For a moment Margret thought Carl was going to object to the plan, because he frowned and gave her an acid stare. Then he shrugged.

'Okay,' he murmured, turning to Laura. 'Shall we start walking now?'

The westering sun was turning the sky apricot colour and changing the sea to beaten gold, when the car Brett was driving dipped down a hill into the old seaport of Camden under the high drooping branches of elm trees, which shaded elegant clapboard houses. They dined on delicious seafood in a restaurant overlooking a harbour crowded with sailing yachts of all sizes, and afterwards made their way through the soft star-sprinkled dusk to the open-air theatre, a semi-circle of grass edged by ghostly silver birches where they sat on low stone terraces.

Soon, with the rest of the audience, Margret was under a spell woven from words by a poet long ago in a country thousands of miles away across the ocean and entangled in a story of lighthearted romance. For the next few hours she lost her identity and became various characters in the play.

First she was Titania, queen of the fairies, complaining to her husband Oberon about his most recent infidelity. Then she was Helena, a young Greek woman, sighing for Demetrius to return her love. And lastly she was Hermia, bitter and spiteful, lashing out at everyone when she discovered that her lover Lysander had apparently fallen out of love with her and had fallen in love with Helena who was now also adored by Demetrius.

'You get my point about the little drama which took place at Lindley's Point, ten years ago, being similar to the play we've just seen?' Brett asked as they drove back along the winding coast road. 'Without the help of love potions, of course,' he added with a laugh.

'I think I do,' she replied, looking at the moonlight silvering the sea. 'But the real life drama didn't have a happy ending. Greg and Liza's marriage was hell on earth, according to him. He was going to divorce her on the grounds of adultery when she was injured in that accident.'

'Then you could say he got his come-uppance for stealing his cousin's girl-friend,' remarked Brett. 'That is, if he did steal her from Carl. It could have been a case of Liza stealing Greg away from Laura. Who knows?'

He dropped her off at Lindley's Point and for a few moments after he had gone she lingered outside the house savouring the beauty of the night. No fog

blotted out the moon or blurred the outline of the
island. Crickets chirped cheerily in the undergrowth. The glittering water sighed languorously and
the wind strummed a love song among the pines at
the back of the house.

> 'In such a night,
>   Stood Dido with a willow in her hand,
>   Upon the wild sea-banks, and waft her love
>   To come again to Carthage.'

Margret whispered the words from another Shakespeare play, from a love scene between Jessica and
Lorenzo in *The Merchant of Venice*. Then with other
fragments of poetry, suitable to the moment, drifting
through her mind, she turned towards the house.

Light streamed out from the living room windows, casting pools of gold on the shadowy sun-
deck. But there was no one in the room and there
was no one in the kitchen either. Switching off the
downstairs lights, she went upstairs and looked into
the room where the children slept. Light from the
landing slanted across their beds. They were empty
and smooth. Where were the children?

Her conscience pricking her because she had left
them, she hurried to the room where Carl had slept
the previous night. Again the slanting light revealed
an empty and unruffled bed. It also glinted on
something lying on top of the chest of drawers. Her
glasses.

On tiptoe she crept towards the chest of drawers,
amused at herself for behaving in such a cautious

way. She picked up the glasses and was just turning to leave the room when the door swung shut, cutting off the light from the landing. Puzzled because the door had closed itself so quietly, she moved towards the line of light she could see showing at the bottom of the door, where it didn't quite fit. She reached out a hand for the knob and then let out a stifled gasp as her hand touched smooth cotton covering a warm throbbing body. Two arms went round her and she began to hit out with both fists as she realised who had hold of her.

'You devil, to scare me like that,' she raged. 'Let me go—oh, let me go!'

'Not yet,' he whispered, one hand sliding beneath her chin while his other arm still held her closely.

'Just what do you think you're doing?' she demanded, still struggling to free herself.

'Welcoming you back,' he said softly, gripping her chin hard so that she could not twist her head. 'Or attempting to undermine your resistance to me, break down that hostility,' he added, his breath wafting across her lips as he laughed. 'You can take your pick.'

Then his lips were on hers, warm and demanding, and strangely all her struggles stopped because, held closely against him, she was finding something for which she seemed to have been searching a long, long time—strength and comfort as well as sensual desire. Response flared up in her, a small flame at first which grew and grew to spread through her, melting all resistance. Her arms curved round him naturally as if it were their right, her hands lifted to his hair, her lips parted beneath his and she felt a long sigh shake through him as at last passion was met with passion.

In the whirling darkness, mouth to mouth they clung, arms binding one to the other, fingers seeking and stroking seductively, and there was no telling where time was. Under the silken skin of their wrists and throats the blood boiled like a torrent and their minds were filled with its roaring sound so that they swayed where they stood. Not until she felt the bed beneath her and heard its springs creak did Margret manage to push Carl away, even though she longed to cling to him longer.

'No,' she whispered, stepping back from the precipice of temptation which yawned before her.

'Why not?' he asked. They were sitting side by side on the bed and she felt his hand at her throat again, sliding round to her nape, tilting her mouth to his. 'If it wasn't for this why did you come in here?'

'To see if you were here.'

'So? I am, and we have the rest of the night to get to know each other some more.' His fingers curled round the edge of the opening of her blouse, the knuckles cool against her skin as they slid downwards. Margret put her hand over his to stop its journey of exploration.

'I came in only to ask you where the children

are,' she said breathlessly. 'I saw my glasses and I
. . . oh, where are they?' She pulled free of him and
sprang to her feet. 'I must have dropped them.' In
the darkness she blundered towards the door and
there was a scrunching sound as she trod on something. 'Please put the light on,' she whispered.

The bedside lamp clicked on. Light shafted down
on to the carpet and glinted on the shattered re-
mains of the glasses under her right foot.

'Now look what you've done!' she wailed, bend-
ing to pick them up. 'They're broken!' Looking up,
she glared at Carl accusingly. Dressed in a dark
green shirt unbuttoned to the waist and tough white
denim pants, he was half lounging on the bed, his
hair and skin glowing gold in the lamplight.

'*I* didn't break them. *You* did when you stepped
on them,' he retorted. 'Let that be a lesson to you
for sneaking into a guy's room uninvited.'

'I didn't sneak!' she flared hotly. 'What have you
done with the children?'

'I haven't *done* anything with them. They're
sleeping over at the Spencer house.'

'You had no right to let them do that without my
permission,' she replied haughtily.

'You left them in Laura's and my charge, so I
reckon we had your permission,' he replied
smoothly. 'They were having a lot of fun with Jack
Spencer's kids who are about the same age and are
staying right now with their grandmother. They'll
be back tomorrow morning, never fear, and then
we'll go cruising.'

'We?' she queried.

'Heather, Jamie and I. I've promised to take them over to Isle au Haut.' He slanted her an underbrowed glance. 'Coming with us?'

'I . . . well, I can't let them go by themselves. I'm paid to look after them,' she faltered.

'Great. It's all fixed, then. We'll go aboard in the morning and set off as soon as there's enough water for us to clear the rocks in the entrance to the pool.'

'But we'll have to be back on Friday before Greg comes,' she said, and became aware of the broken glasses in her hand. 'Oh, what am I going to do?' she whispered. 'Once he sees me without them he'll know I deliberately deceived him.'

Swinging off the bed, Carl came towards her and took the shattered glasses from her to examine them.

'Why did you wear them in the first place?' he asked. 'Why did you pretend to be different from what you are?'

Between their tawny lashes his eyes seemed very dark in the lamplight. He wasn't handsome in the way Greg was. His features were too roughly-hewn, the nose too big and bold, the chin too square, and the twist to his lip gave him a perpetually satirical expression, as if he were secretly and unkindly laughing at the mistakes and weaknesses of other people. But his eyes were beautiful, large and well-shaped under heavy lids, their colour changing from clear, brilliant aquamarine to a warm and burning indigo according to his mood.

'I needed a job, desperately,' she explained. 'The

play I'd been acting in was taken off after a week because it flopped.'

'You're an actress?'

'I was.' Her soft lips quirked in a self-disparaging smile. 'It took me three years to find out I would only ever be fourth rate and I became tired of being hungry, so I looked around for something different to do. Greg was having difficulty in finding someone to take care of Heather and Jamie after Liza had deserted him. I asked for my name to be put forward and the woman at the agency said that if I really wanted the job I should make myself look older, so. . . .' She broke off, shrugging her shoulders.

'So you put on an act,' Carl finished for her. 'And not a very good one.'

'It was good enough to get me the job, and Greg has never questioned me about my age,' she retorted spiritedly.

'He wouldn't,' he jeered. 'Why should he if you're doing what he wants, looking after his children, keeping house for him, doing all the things a wife usually does without making the demands a wife would make, as Liza probably made? Why should he upset the nice cosy applecart you've been making for him in return for your keep?'

'Now you're being deliberately unpleasant,' she said in a choked voice. 'You're jealous of Greg and resent him because . . . well, because he stole Liza from you.'

'Did he?' His eyebrows went up and he laughed.

The warmth had gone from his eyes and they glinted at her with cold mockery as he stepped closer to her. 'You've been cheating,' he accused.

'What do you mean?'

'You've been getting to know me behind my back instead of directly. You've been listening to gossip. It's true Liza was my girl first and I brought her here. I liked her and she was good company for someone like me who was recuperating from a bloody awful war. But I guess I didn't play the game her way and Greg did.' He studied the glasses in his hand. 'What do you think he'll do when he finds out about your deception?' he asked.

'He might sack me.'

'And if he does, what will you do then?' he asked, his lashes flicking up as he looked at her curiously.

'I'm not sure. It might be difficult for me to get a job over here.'

'That's true, since you're an alien. Would you go back to England?'

'I suppose I'd have to.'

'And take up acting again.'

'No. Oh, I love the theatre. I love watching plays and films. I like identifying with the characters, but I don't want to project them any more. I prefer being myself all the time.'

'I'd always thought that people who go in for acting can never give it up. They become addicted to it.'

'I've never been like that,' she said, 'so I suppose

I'm not really talented.'

'Then why did you go in for it?'

'When I left school at sixteen, I was most un-happy. My father had just married again and I was jealous of my stepmother. She laughed when I said I wanted to be an actress and I had to go in for it then, just to prove to her that I could be.'

'A modern Cinderella?' he asked scoffingly.

'No, never. I didn't stay at home hoping to be rescued from my unhappiness by some Prince Charming offering me marriage,' she retorted.

'So you don't see marriage as a way of solving your problem if Greg sacks you and you have to go back to England?' he queried.

'I couldn't marry just because I found myself out of work. I couldn't marry . . . not without love,' she said vehemently.

'Not without love,' he repeated slowly. 'What does that mean?'

'I couldn't marry a man unless I loved him,' she replied.

'Waiting for Mr Right, eh?' Again his tone was mocking. 'Think you'll recognise him when he comes along?'

'I'm sure I shall, and I can tell you now he won't be a bit like you,' she said sharply, disturbed by his taunts. She turned away to the door and opened it. 'It's late. I must go to bed,' she added determinedly.

'Can't I interest you in sharing this bed with me?' Carl was there, in front of her again, moving in on her with that catlike stealth, his hands reaching for her waist, his eyes gleaming darkly between their lashes, his lips parting sensually, and to her utmost irritation her heart began to hammer with excitement. 'In spite of what you say to my face I know you feel differently, Margret,' he said softly. 'And I think we'd make a pretty good partnership.'

'Well, I don't, and I'm not interested at all in sharing a bed with you, ever!' She pushed free of him and somehow got through the door, banging it shut before he could follow her.

Reaching her bedroom, she closed the door and, thankful that there was a key, turned it in the lock. She didn't trust Carl Lindley at all. He was bold enough to follow her into this room and continue to make outrageous suggestions to her. Share his bed with him, indeed!

But her heart leapt again with excitement at the thought of making love with him in the moon-dappled darkness. Her skin tingled and her lips parted and trembled, and she gasped for breath as she remembered the touch of his hands and lips. Never had she felt like this before. Never had she been overwhelmed by physical desire. But it was overwhelming her now so that she ached and throbbed with a longing to get up and go to Carl's room again.

It couldn't be happening to her. She couldn't possibly be falling in love with a man she had met only twenty-four hours ago. She must think of something else, about Greg and what he would say when he returned on Friday and saw her without her glasses. Several times she forced herself to go through an imaginary scene with him, inventing what he would say and what she would answer, acting it out in her mind until at last she fell asleep.

She dreamed about the play she had seen, believing herself to be Hermia, running through the woods with Lysander, who looked like Greg. They were hand in hand, but suddenly he pulled his hand from hers and began to run after another woman, who was tall, with bright blonde hair and wide grey eyes that looked like tiny frozen lakes—Laura Spencer. She would have pulled Greg away from Laura, but an arm, broad and sinewy and furred with golden hairs, came round her neck from behind and she was jerked backwards and carried off to a dark cave.

Sweating and muttering, entangled in the sheet, she came awake to the sound of banging on the door. She opened her eyes to yellow sunlight and knew it was late. She had overslept.

'Margret!' Carl's voice was harsh as he called through the door. 'Wake up! It's past ten o'clock and Heather and Jamie are here. They're raring to go on the yacht and if you don't get up soon we'll go cruising without you.'

Unwinding the sheet from about her, Margret scrambled off the bed and hurried over to the door. She unlocked and opened it and felt a dangerous delight surge through her at this first meeting of the day with Carl. But he was not feeling the same pleasure in seeing her, apparently. His mouth twisted unpleasantly and his eyes were like chips of blue ice between narrowed lids.

'You didn't have to lock the door,' he said through taut lips. 'I don't go in for rape.'

She stiffened and and her chin tilted challengingly.

'Since you'd made it clear that you do what you want to do without ever asking permission I thought it would be wiser if I did,' she jibed, and saw the bone whiten the skin along his jaw as he gritted his teeth. 'You mustn't take the children on the yacht without me.'

'Okay. I won't take them without you if you'll get dressed, pack a change of clothes and be down on the shore ready to go in fifteen minutes,' he retorted coldly. 'They're all ready to go and so am I.'

'But. . . .' she began.

'See you on the shore,' he said coolly, striding off towards the stairs.

'But I don't . . . I haven't. . . .' she spluttered.

'We'll go without you,' he taunted, and disappeared down the stairs.

Millie was right about him, Margret thought furiously as she dressed quickly in jeans and shirt. He was too fond of riding roughshod. But she couldn't let him take Heather and Jamie without her. Greg wouldn't be pleased if she did, she was sure.

Carl was just about to push off in the dinghy when she arrived breathless on the shore. He ordered her to sit in the bow, and pretending she was accustomed to moving about on boats and that she wasn't alarmed by the quivering of the rubber floor of the dinghy, she stepped past the children and sat down on the hard air-packed bow.

It would be an experience, she thought, as the dinghy bounced over the waves, some of which slopped over the bow to wet her, one she might never get again, to go sailing over the glittering blue sea to those distant islands that beckoned so temptingly. It would be an adventure, and suddenly her spirits soared and her heart sang for no reason she could think of.

CHAPTER THREE

THE cove was an almost landlocked pool of clear water edged by rocks of pink and grey granite, some overgrown by golden-brown rockweed. Here and there the rocks gave way to tiny beaches of pale sandy shingle, backed by thick woods of spruce and cedar, a half-lit world where birds whistled in the soft warm air of the morning.

When she leaned over the wire lifelines which ran round the sides of the yacht Margret could see right to the bottom of the water to ochre-coloured sand strewn with rocks and shells where small fishes swam about with tiny flicks of the tails. Near to the shore the water was a dark olive green where it reflected the trees and it was disturbed by a series of whirl-pools, showing that the current was strong there as the tide ebbed.

The cove was situated on Isle au Haut, one of the islands which were part of the Acadia National Park, an area which covered stretches of forests and lakes on the mainland as well as some islands; an idyllic place which was well named, where the beauty of nature was protected and preserved for the enjoyment of everyone who visited it; a place where the sea dominated every view; where lobster boats churned along coasts picking up traps and the bells of navigation buoys tolled day and night warning fishermen and sailors of the dangers to be found on the rugged rocky shores.

After three days of cruising about the islands Margret knew much more about them than she had when she had set off. She knew now that over four hundred years ago the islands had provided shelter for the many fishermen who had come regularly across the Atlantic in their small ships from England, France, Spain and Portugal to fish on the productive banks that lay under the sea, and slowly they had built up small settlements. Later the explorers had come, amongst them the great Samuel Champlain whose men had named this particular island Isle au Haut because it had been higher than the others scattered around it.

After making sure that Jamie was safe and happy, sitting on the foredeck and fishing with the rod Carl had given him, Margret walked along the deck to the cockpit and stretched out on one of the long seats to let the sun warm her bare limbs. Pillowing her head on her folded arms, she closed her eyes. Today was Sunday and Greg would have been back at Lindley's Point for a day and a half.

When she had realised on Friday afternoon that Carl had no intention of returning to the mainland that day she had been very disturbed.

'But we must go back. We must be there when he comes,' she had remonstrated. 'He'll expect us to be there and when we're not he'll wonder what's happened to us. He'll worry.'

'No, he won't,' Carl had been imperturbable. 'Laura will be there when he arrives. She'll tell him where we've gone.'

They had been anchored in another cove, at the head of a long inlet on Deer Island, several miles in from the sea and completely sheltered from any wind. They hadn't been far in actual miles from Lindley's Point, but the place had been accessible only by boat and there hadn't been any way Margret and the children could have returned to the house. At the time Margret had asked Carl what time they would leave the anchorage and he had replied that they would stay there for the night, they had all been ashore on a rocky islet, searching for shells and other remnants of sea life.

'Then we must go back tomorrow morning, first thing,' she had insisted, but he hadn't answered her and had strolled off along the narrow beach, after the children. Lips tight, irritated by his coolness, she had gone after him. 'We must go back tomorrow morning—do you hear me?' she had demanded.

'I hear you,' he had retorted, swinging round to face her, and his twisted smile had mocked her. 'But I'm not going back to Lindley's tomorrow morning just because Greg will be there. I came up here on this boat to cruise among the islands, so I'm going to have my cruise. Tomorrow we'll go on to Isle au Haut and stay for a night. We'll probably sail back to Lindley's on Monday. I have to return this boat to its owner at Camden on Wednesday or Thursday, so I'll have to start down the coast on Tuesday at the latest.'

'You shouldn't have brought us with you if you had no intention of returning today,' she had argued.

'But I wanted to bring you—particularly you—with me,' he countered softly, leaning towards her. 'I like having you around, even when you're putting on that act of being a prim and proper Mary Poppins, like now.'

'It isn't an act!' she had flung at him.

'No?' his eyebrows had tilted satirically. 'I think it is. I've held you in my arms and felt the passion that boils beneath your cool, demure appearance. You're no storybook nanny, you're a real live woman with a woman's natural instincts and desires, and right now you're longing to fulfil those desires. You're ripe for the picking, Margret.'

'I . . . oh, I hate you!' she had whispered fiercely, her cheeks burning.

'Because I've seen through your act?' he taunted. 'Well, hate is better than indifference. It means you're aware of me as someone to be reckoned with.'

She had walked away from him then, after the children, and had squatted down with them to examine the circular green sea-urchin cases they had discovered, scattered among the rocks, left there by the seagulls.

She hadn't said any more about returning to

Lindley's Point. In fact she had tried hard to ignore Carl for the rest of the day, but it had been difficult in the close confines of the yacht and once the children were in the bunks in the forward cabin and fast asleep there was nowhere else to be except with him in the main cabin where he and she would sleep on the settee berths, separately, of course.

He wasn't a person she could ignore easily. He was too big, too vital, every move he made explosive with energy, and whenever she had looked up from the book she had been reading she had found him watching her, that amused curve to his mouth as if he had guessed how tense she felt in his presence.

'How long do you think you can keep it up?' he had drawled at last, leaving the other settee berth and coming across to sit beside her.

'Keep what up?' She had tried to sound casual, although her skin had begun to tingle and her heart had begun to pound.

'The cold war?' he had mocked.

'Do we have to talk?' she had said with pretended mildness. 'I happen to be reading a very good book that I find extremely interesting.'

'Sure. So interesting that you haven't turned a page for ten whole minutes,' he had jeered.

'It's a pity you haven't anything better to do than sit and watch me read,' she had flared.

'Nothing is better than sitting and watching you except kissing you,' he had replied softly, and taking the thick paperback book from her suddenly nerveless fingers he had tossed it aside, and there had been a short strained silence while they had stared at each other.

Slowly he had bent towards her lips and she hadn't tried to avoid him. His lips had been tangy with sea salt and his skin had smelt of the sun. His touch had been tenderly seductive and had drawn from her an immediate response over which she had had no control. But as soon as she realised she had responded she had withdrawn, moving back, away from him, afraid of what was going on inside her; afraid of her leaping pulses and quivering nerves.

'Still hating me?' he had whispered, leaning sideways against the cushioned back of the berth.

'Yes.' Her wary glance had swerved sidelong to his face and away again. 'No,' she had muttered hastily, remembering what he had said about preferring her hate to her indifference. Then, covering her hot cheeks with her hands, she cried out, 'Oh, I don't know. I've never met anyone like you before, and I don't know whether to take what you say and do seriously or not.'

'Why bother to try?' he had argued. 'Take each moment as it comes. Be yourself and do what you *feel* like doing instead of trying to analyse any motives I might have. I'm not analysing why I feel like making love to you nor why I kissed you just now. I wanted to do it, so I did it.'

Again she had given him a sideways glance, had looked down at her hands and then back at him again, studying from under her down-sweeping lashes the shape of his mouth, the strong clean line of bone in his neck, the enticing glimpse of his tanned chest within the shadows cast by the un-buttoned opening of his shirt, and she had felt desire gnaw within her low down, a desire to reach out and touch him, to rouse his passion until it got beyond his control and overwhelmed them both.

Amazed by her feelings, she had looked away quickly, her hands gripping one another on her lap as she sought to subdue her desires.

'I'd like to go to bed,' she had muttered.

'With me?' Quick as a flash, his query had come, startling her, making her realise how easily her statement could be misunderstood.

'No—oh no. That isn't what I mean.' She had seen mockery lurking about his mouth and eyes and had burst out, 'Oh, that's why I dislike you so much! You twist what I say to suit your own ends. I meant that I feel sleepy and I'd like to get into my berth, but I can't because you're sitting on it.'

Carl hadn't moved immediately but had con-tinued to survey her with narrowed eyes, his head tilted back against the side of the berth, his wind-roughened hair contrasting brightly with the dark red upholstery.

'If we did sleep together, I'd be the first, wouldn't I?' he had asked quietly.

'But we're not. . . .' she had begun hotly and de-fensively, even while her pulses leapt again at the thought of sleeping with him. 'Yes, you would,' she admitted, changing her tune.

'And you'd prefer to be married first, before taking a step like that?' he suggested.

'Is there anything wrong in that?' she had retorted, sensing mockery again.

'No, not really,' he had replied equably. 'If I were the marrying kind of man I expect I would prefer to marry a woman who hadn't indulged in pre-marital sex.'

'But you're not the marrying kind,' she had retorted sharply.

'You've got it,' he said with an enigmatic grin, and rising to his feet he began to pull the berth out to make it wide enough for her to sleep on. 'Sleep well,' he had said, turning away, and had gone up through the hatchway to the deck, leaving her to prepare for bed alone, her thoughts swirling in all directions.

The night had passed peacefully and next morning they had sailed down the long inlet to the sea, the wind behind them filling the two white sails, the water, glittering in the sunlight, tinkling under the bow and gurgling past the stern. Under a blue sky streaked by feathery white clouds the shores of the inlet had glowed yellow and the blue-green woods of spruce and cedar trees had been spangled with the silvery trunks and golden leaves of silver birches. As the boat approached them long-necked, long-beaked blue-black cormorants ducked beneath the surface of the water or took off with much flapping of their wide wings. White and grey gulls had stood silently on almost submerged yellow rocks or had circled and shouted above the ledges of high cliffs. And everywhere, along the edges of the shores, bobbing on the waves, trap buoys had been flashes of bright colour, poised like exotic birds.

When they had reached this cove where there was only room enough and water enough for one boat to swing, they had gone ashore at once to explore the woods, returning to the boat to barbecue steaks and later to sit in the cockpit and watch the sunset colour the sky and the sea crimson, lemon and purple.

It had been a perfect day, one Margret would not easily forget, and under its spell she had relaxed the restraints she had imposed on herself and had given herself fully to it, behaving naturally, enjoying every moment, learning from Carl how to sail the boat, about the history of the islands, finding a new and deep joy in sharing that time with him.

Yet when darkness had come creeping stealthily over the land and water, remembering what had happened the previous evening, distrusting not only him but also herself, she had arranged for Jamie to sleep in the main cabin on the settee berth she had used and had moved her things into the small forward cabin. As soon as both children were tucked up she had said a cool goodnight to Carl and had gone to bed, shutting the door between the two cabins; shutting him out.

But she had not been able to shut him out of her thoughts, and he was in them now as she lay with her eyes closed, feeling the heat of the sun on her eyelids, listening to the soft sigh of water against the hull of the boat, hoping he would return soon. He had gone ashore with Heather for one last walk through the woods and she had stayed behind with Jamie because the little boy had not wanted to go but preferred to fish.

Splash! The sound was followed by her name being screamed by Jamie. Starting up, she looked round. He wasn't where she had left him on the foredeck.

'Margret, Mar . . .!' The rest of her name was swallowed in a horrible gurgling sound. Alarm racing through her, Margret bounded up on to the side deck and looking over saw, to her horror, that Jamie was in the water and was being swept towards the narrow entrance of the cove by the sinister stealthy current, the life-preserver that Carl had insisted the child wear all the time he was on the boat glowing orange against the blue-green of the water.

'Jamie, kick your legs and try to swim this way!' she called to him, but doubted if he could hear her. She couldn't go after him in the dinghy because that was on the shore. There was only one way to get to him before he was swept out to sea. She would have to swim.

Down into the cabin she jumped, grabbed her

own life-preserver and snapped it on. From the
bookcase she took out the bugle-shaped foghorn and
rushed up the steps to the cockpit again. Three
times she blew on the horn, a signal arranged by
Carl should any of them require help when he was
ashore. Then she stripped off her jeans and sneakers
and, standing on the boat rail at the opening in the
lifelines, she drew a deep breath and plunged.

The water was much colder than she had expected, causing her to gasp as it closed over her
head so that she swallowed some of it. Spluttering
and coughing, she clawed to the surface, realising
that she would have to keep moving to avoid becoming thoroughly chilled and so unable to operate
properly. Striking out with an over-arm crawl, she
swam after the bobbing orange life-preserver which
was all she could see of Jamie.

The swift ebbing current caught at her, whirling
her onwards, and soon she was beside Jamie. He
had stopped kicking and was floating quite pas-
sively, supported by the life-preserver. But his eyes
were closed and his lips had a bluish tinge. When
she spoke to him he didn't answer, and she guessed
that the icy water had numbed him. Panic chilling
her as much as the water, she gathered him against
her, supporting him with her hands, her body floating under his and, kicking hard with both legs, she
started off in the direction of the boat, hoping she
had the strength to beat the tide.

Slowly and inexorably they were carried past the

jagged rocks that protected the entrance of the cove and she could hear the thunder of waves breaking on ledges outside the cove. She could imagine them foaming white on long black reefs before sliding back glassily in retreat. She felt the undertow curl round her legs, icy cold. She and Jamie were being dragged out to sea and she wanted to shout for Carl. But how could he hear her if he were in the forest? *Carl, Carl. Please come now.* The words repeated themselves over and over in her mind like a prayer.

Vaguely, as in a dream, she heard his voice and tried to look round, only to have a wave slap into her face, causing her to choke. Then a dark shape came between her and the shore as the rubber dinghy slithered over the water, and she saw Heather's face, square and fair, looking down at her.

'I'll take Jamie.' Carl spoke calmly as if picking people out of the water was an everyday occurrence for him. 'Hold on to the dinghy.'

His arms reached down and Jamie was lifted from her. She clung to the thin rope which was looped round the outside of the dinghy and was used for carrying it.

'Now you,' said Carl.

Feeling like a fish being landed, she was pulled over the side, puffing and panting.

'What happened?' Carl demanded, beginning to row with long strong strokes.

'I don't know,' she croaked. In spite of the warm sun she was cold, shivering with reaction. 'I don't know.' She looked at Jamie, who was lying without moving against the sturdy Heather. 'I hope he didn't drown. Greg will never forgive me if he's drowned.'

'He's okay, still breathing but a bit cold and shocked,' said Carl. 'He'll be okay once we get him aboard and into his sleeping bag. Same goes for you.'

At last the dark blue hull of the yacht loomed over them. Heather went aboard first, then Margret, who reached out to help Jamie. Down in the cabin Carl stripped off Jamie's wet clothing and rubbed him dry roughly with a towel, teasing the little boy, making him laugh, doing anything to banish the shocked look from his eyes.

Margret went into the forward cabin intending to take off her wet shirt and panties, but when she got there all she could do was sink down on the edge of a bunk and shiver. She was still sitting there shaking when Carl came through the door. He gave her one assessing glance and stepped out again, coming back with a big towel. Closing the door, he spoke sharply.

'Get that shirt off and I'll rub you dry.'

'No,' she objected weakly as he sat down beside her.

'Yes,' he retorted. 'There's nothing to be gained by being coy now. Or by being stubborn.' His fingers pulled undone the buttons of the shirt. He eased it off her shoulders and wrapped the towel around her bare body. 'You took a chance, you know, jumping into that water.' He began to rub her roughly, his hands hard and impersonal through the towel. 'It never gets very warm, even at the height of summer, because of the cold current that sweeps down this coast from the north. Margret, stop it!' His arm went round her shaking shoulders and he drew her close to him. 'It's all over now,' he said softly, his cheek against hers. 'It's all right, so stop crying.'

'I ... I ... can't,' she hiccuped. 'Jamie could have drowned. Oh, what's Greg going to say when he knows? I should have been watching. Oh, I can't do anything properly! I can't even take care of a little boy. It's all my fault. He could have drowned. He could have drowned!'

'So could you have drowned,' he said roughly. 'But neither of you did. And if anyone is to blame, it's me.'

'You?' Surprise acted like a slap in the face, stopping her mounting hysteria suddenly. She raised her head to stare at him. 'I don't understand.'

'Jamie couldn't have fallen off the boat unless he'd gotten under the lifelines somehow. And he didn't do that. He's just told me he got tired of fishing from the bow and decided to try from the side-deck. He stood in the opening of the lifelines and fished from there. He thought he had a bite and he leaned over to see, lost his balance and fell in. Now if I'd fastened the lifelines when Heather and I left the boat, as I should have done, he wouldn't have fallen in.'

'But I should have noticed they were unfastened,'

Margret argued. She had stopped shivering now, but had no desire to move out of the comforting circle of his arm. 'It was my fault.'

'Let's share the blame, shall we?' he said. 'Neither of us is perfect. Feeling warmer now?'

'Yes, thank you. I . . . I'm sorry I broke down.'

His calm matter-of-factness was soothing. She should be moving away from him, but now that she was coming out of the shock she felt drowsy. She nestled her head against his shoulder. Under the towel his hand was warm against her bare skin, the fingers spreading close to her breast. She should push his hand away, but suddenly she didn't care any more that she had practically nothing on and he was holding her. She wanted to stay with him for another hour or so, lie on the bunk and sleep, held in his arms. Never had she felt so close to anyone. Never had she wanted to be with anyone as much as she wanted to be with him.

Unthinkingly, obeying some deep primitive urge, she tipped her head back to look at him, her lips parting slightly in invitation. Carl's glance swerved down to her face. His eyes darkened, he muttered something under his breath and then his other hand was in her wet hair, gripping the back of her head, and his mouth was claiming hers in a kiss whose hot violence expressed for both of them their longing to be closer to each other.

'Margret, Jamie wants you to read a story to him!' The door rattled and Heather's voice was imperative.

Margret pulled free from Carl and dragged the damp towel about her.

'All right. I'll come when I've changed my clothes,' she called out. She turned to Carl. 'I'm all right now,' she whispered to him. 'I can manage.'

'There have been times on this cruise when I've wished I could have left Heather at Lindley's Point,' he said wryly. 'And this is one of them,' he added, heaving to his feet. 'You don't have to read to Jamie—I'll read to him. You get into your sleeping bag and have a rest, get warm. Later we'll go back to Lindley's. The wind is piping up and it should be a fast sail back.'

For once Margret did as he had ordered. She climbed into her sleeping bag and curling up in the bunk fell asleep almost at once. She wakened much later to the violent rolling and pitching of the boat and a queasy feeling in her stomach. The boat was sailing. For a while she lay, reluctant to leave the nest of eiderdown in which she was cocooned, thinking of Carl, imagining what would have happened if Heather hadn't interrupted them and groaning at her own weak and wanton behaviour.

What was the matter with her? Why had she invited him to kiss and touch her? Was it only the day before yesterday she had told him she hated him? Was it only yesterday she had rejected his suggestion that they sleep together for the third time since she had met him? She must be going out of her mind, and lying here imagining what would have happened if Heather hadn't called to her wasn't helping at all.

Unzipping the sleeping bag, she rolled out of it and dressed as well as she was able because the motion of the boat made standing up difficult and she kept having to put out her hands to prevent herself from being slammed against the bunks. As soon as she was decent in clean jeans and shirt she went into the main cabin, hanging on to the wooden hand rails. Jamie was rolled up in his sleeping bag on the settee berth and Carl had fixed the leeboards at the side of the berth so that the little boy wouldn't fall out. Up in the cockpit Heather was standing at the wheel, holding it, a expression of smug satisfaction on her face as she steered the boat. Behind her Carl stood keeping a watchful eye on what she was doing.

The weather had changed. Grey clouds were rolling in from the south west, reaching out greedy wispy fingers for the sun, which had now become a pale disc of watery yellow. The wind was increasing steadily, lashing the water into crested waves, which seemed to be piling up behind the boat. White sails full, the yacht was leaping over the sea, sparkling spray flying over its bow, creaming surf gurgling past its leeward rail.

'How far to Lindley's Point?' Margret asked, as she balanced on the top step of the companionway, sheltering in the hatchway from the wind.

By way of answer Carl pointed in the direction of the bow and looking that way she saw across the heaving grey water the familiar dark hump of Hog's Back Island.

'Another hour and we'll be there,' said Carl. 'If you're coming out here you'll need sweater, jacket and oilskins,' he went on in his practical way. 'It isn't any too warm and spray comes over occasionally to soak us.'

She was tempted to join him, to share the wild, exhilarating sail with him, but Jamie called to her, saying he felt sick, so she denied herself the luxury of being with Carl and returned to the cabin to attend to the little boy. By the time he had been sick in the bucket she found she was feeling ill herself and was glad to go up into the cockpit again for a few moments, to breathe in the fresh salty air. Both Carl and Heather seemed to be thoroughly enjoying the excitement of the sailing, and for the first time it occurred to Margret as she looked from Heather to Carl, and back again to Heather, that the girl was more like Carl than she was like her own father, Greg. She had the same lion-like colouring of hair and skin, the same self-confidence and fearlessness, the same practical outlook on life. Heather could be Carl's child!

The thought startled her so much that she had to go below again. Heather could be Carl's daughter. After all, Liza had been his girl-friend and they had probably been lovers. As she sat beside Jamie, holding his hand, Margret felt her stomach curdle. But it wasn't seasickness which was causing her to feel sour suddenly. It was jealousy, plain old-fashioned jealousy because a woman she had never met and who was now dead had once been Carl's girl-friend and had probably known him intimately.

Then why had Liza run away with Greg? Why had she married him? Had she discovered Carl wasn't the marrying kind and so had turned to Greg, in order to find a father for her child? Had Liza told Carl she was expecting his child and had he turned her down? Margret shook her head, trying to clear it of such unpleasant thoughts, wishing they had never entered it.

She became aware that the boat wasn't tipping over quite so much and looking through one of the portholes saw that they were turning past the long rocky spit that ran out into the sea from the end of Hog's Back Island. The engine throbbed into life and Carl called to her to come up into the cockpit to steer the boat while he took down the sails. Soon the boat was slipping past the dark, wicked rocks that almost encircled the pool of deep water which was the anchorage.

'I can see Daddy!' Heather cried excitedly, waving her arm. 'Look, Margret, can you see him? He's come out on the sun-deck.'

Margaret looked over towards the old grey house hiding among the apple trees. She could see Greg and someone else, someone tall and blonde. Laura Spencer.

'Are you ready to go ashore?' Carl asked briskly.

'I haven't packed my bag yet,' she said quickly. 'I'll go and do it now.'

She went down below and hurried to the forward cabin, hearing Carl talking to Jamie in the main cabin behind her.

'If Heather's bag is packed I'll take her and Jamie ashore now and come back for you,' said Carl.

'Yes, it's packed,' she replied, handing it to him. 'But I won't be long.'

'Rowing ashore in this wind will be easier if there are fewer of us in the dinghy at a time,' he said. 'I'll be back, never fear.'

Now that the short cruise was over she was wishing quite contrarily that it could have lasted longer, Margret thought as she rolled and stuffed her wet clothing into the bag and then began to roll up the sleeping bag. She was wishing she could stay aboard and sail with Carl down the coast.

God, what was she thinking of now? With a hand to her cheek she sank down on the side of the bunk. She couldn't stay with him, not just because she had to go ashore and look after the children for Greg but also because it wasn't safe for her to be with Carl. With a few whispered words and a few provocative caresses he was able to bewitch her, change her from the cool self-contained, self-controlled person she tried so hard to be into an impulsive woman who was ruled by emotion and desire. And instead of wanting to go with him she should be glad he would be leaving Lindley's Point tomorrow. She should be glad he was going out of her life for ever.

He seemed to be a long time coming back for her. Several times she went up to the cockpit to look across the narrow stretch of water, across the rim of pale sandy beach to the grey house before she saw the dinghy coming. She had gone down into the cabin to collect her bag when she heard the dinghy bump against the side. At once she went up into the cockpit. Carl climbed aboard, tied up the dinghy and stepped down into the cockpit, slanting her a bright curious glance, his mouth twisting into a smile.

'We're alone at last,' he said. 'Shall I pull up the anchor and set sail again, right now? There's a small harbour on the other side of the reach where we could spend the night. And tomorrow we could set off down the coast together? Shall we go, just you and I, and sail to the ends of the earth?'

His suggestion was so close to her own recent thoughts that she could only stare at him in amazement. Then, thinking he was mocking her, she turned away sharply, muttering,

'Don't make fun!'

'I'm not making fun,' he said, stepping round in front of her. 'I mean it, Margret. Sail with me today and tomorrow to Camden, then fly with me to Peru.'

'To Peru?' Her heart jolted against her ribs. 'Why should I do that?'

'To live with me there, share bed and board with me.'

'Now I know you're crazy,' she retorted. 'We've known each other barely six days and you're asking me to . . . to. . . .' She broke off, unable to put into words what she was thinking.

'To elope with me?' His mouth twisted in a grin of self-derision. 'I guess I am. It must run in the family.' He put his hands on her waist and drew her towards him. 'Shall I pull up the anchor? Shall we go?'

'No. I can't go without seeing Greg. I have to explain to him about Jamie,' she said quickly, erecting barriers between them again, afraid of the wild impulse that was surging through her; an impulse which seemed to shout loudly, *Go. Go with him.*

'Heather has already told him. There wasn't any way I could stop her from blurting it out. She's damned arrogant for her age,' he said tautly.

'She's like you,' she said, seizing quickly at another straw to pile on the protective barrier. 'In many ways.'

Carl gave her a wary glance.

'Meaning?' His voice purred threateningly. It seemed he didn't like being compared to his young cousin.

'She could be your daughter. She's more like you than she's like Greg,' she said coolly. It was the way to strengthen her resistance to him, she thought. She would dwell on the more unpleasant aspects of his character, keep alive her initial dislike of him. Turning away from him again, she went down the steps into the cabin to fetch her bag, twisting her hair into its tight knot at her nape in readiness for meeting Greg.

When she turned round, bag in hand, to go up the steps she found Carl half way down them, barring her way.

'I catch your drift,' he said softly between taut lips, his eyes glittering with anger. 'You're implying that I made Liza pregnant and then refused to take the responsibility, so she turned to Greg.' He came down the rest of the steps to tower over her. 'Jealous of her?' he taunted.

'No, I'm not,' she lied.

'Then why think it? Why insult me like that?' he challenged.

'Is it an insult?' she countered.

'Sure it is. I don't go around getting women with child and then walk away from them,' he said between his teeth. 'I can see the resemblance in Heather to me, but she doesn't look like me because I'm her father. She takes after her grandfather, Greg's father and my father's brother. It's a family resemblance. Most of the Lindleys are big and fair. In any case, Heather couldn't be my child. She was born a year too late for her ever to have been mine. She's Greg's child. My affair with Liza was over some time before she went away with Greg.' He approached her closely and leaned forward, his face near to hers. 'Take it back,' he suggested quietly, and his quietness was much more threatening than any noisy show of anger would have been.

'If I do will you take me ashore to see Greg?'

'So you won't come with me?' he persisted.

'No, I can't. I have to see him,' she replied steadily. 'I'm sorry I said what I did about Heather being your daughter. It was mean and spiteful of me. Please will you take me ashore now?'

'After this.'

She could have dodged him, but she didn't want to. She let him take her in his arms and even offered her lips to his. At his touch her senses reeled and for a few moments she was oblivious to everything except the tender provocation of his kiss and the warmth of his embrace. Slowly he lifted his mouth from hers and holding her tightly, his cheek against her hair he whispered,

'Come, fly with me to Peru, Margret. We could have a lot of fun together.'

'For how long?' she asked shakily, close to capitulation to his demands.

'For as long as we both want.'

'I can't give you an answer now. I have to go ashore to see Greg.'

'Okay.' He released her, looking down at her with eyes which had a dark brooding expression in them. He picked up her bag. 'Come on, we'll go ashore.'

Greg was waiting for them when the dinghy crunched aground on the shore.

'Are you all right, Margret?' he asked, his dark eyes expressing concern as he helped her out of the dinghy. 'Carl says you went into the water after Jamie and that it's thanks to you Jamie wasn't swept out to sea and drowned.'

'I'm all right now, thank you,' she said. Nothing was happening. She was pleased to see him again, but not excited, nor, strangely enough, apprehensive about what he might say when he noticed she looked different.

'Did you lose your glasses when you dove in?' he asked, his eyebrows slanting together in a frown of puzzlement.

'No. I . . . er . . . well, I broke them.'

'You look very different without them,' he said, staring at her as if he had never seen her before. 'Very different. Can you see all right?'

'Yes, I can see. And I can explain everything. You see. . . .'

'Later, later,' he said. 'I've a lot to tell you too, but right now I think I'd better help Carl bring the dinghy up. I guess you'd like to shower and change. Laura is up at the house seeing to Heather and Jamie. You've met her, haven't you?'

'Yes, I've met her.'

He was just the same, Margret thought as she went towards the house, avoiding something he had sensed might create difficulties for him, putting off

until later explanations and decisions, not really
wanting to hear the explanations, not really wanting to make any decisions.

In the house Laura was just coming down the
stairs with a well-scrubbed, well-brushed Jamie who
was neatly dressed in dark blue pants of polyester
and cotton knit and a matching T-shirt. Laura's ice-
grey glance flicked over Margret's creased jeans,
crumpled nylon windbreaker and untidy windblown
hair, which was falling out of the hasty knot into
which she had twisted it.

'You don't look much better than Heather and
Jamie did, when they came ashore,' Laura drawled
critically. Her blonde hair regulated into stiff waves
sweeping back from her deeply tanned face, she was
as elegantly turned out as usual in a white blazer
suit with a pleated skirt and navy blue blouse. 'But I
expect you're tired after today's unfortunate epi-
sode, so I'll take the children off your hands this
evening. They can come with us to dinner at the
Fishermen's Inn at Roskeag. Carl is coming too.
It will be quite like old times for him, Greg and
me, and it will give you some time to recover.'
Laura turned to look up the stairs. 'Are you
ready, Heather?' she called.

Also looking well scrubbed and well brushed, her
blonde hair plaited into two perky pigtails, Heather
came downstairs looking rather selfconscious in her
only summer dress, made from cotton patterned
with tiny blue flowers, which Margret had never

been able to persuade her to wear, the girl always preferring to dress in jeans and T-shirts.

Laura's face creased into a rather patronising smile as she looked back at Margret.

'It was good of you to take them on the cruise with Carl,' she said. 'It's meant such a lot to me, being able to talk to Greg. We've been able to get to know each other again. See you later.'

It was natural that old friends should want to go out to dinner together, thought Margret as she plodded up the stairs, but she couldn't help feeling as if she had been deliberately left out of their plans. Yet being alone for a few hours would give her a chance to consider Carl's invitation to go with him to Peru, to come to terms with her new self, the woman he had bewitched with his rough magic and who longed to go with him to the ends of the earth but who was afraid to follow her instincts.

CHAPTER FOUR

THE wind storm blew itself out in the night and next morning dawned still and clear. From her bedroom window Margret could see the contours of Deer Island and could even believe she could recognise the wooded hills around the inlet where she had spent the day and a night with Carl and the children.

Her glance left the distant sunlit curves and focussed on the narrow strait of water, on the dark blue boat riding at anchor in the deep pool. Behind the yacht the rubber dinghy indicated that Carl was still on board. He must have stayed the night on the boat, because he hadn't come in with Greg and the children when they had returned.

Marget had expected to have some discussion with Greg after the children had gone to bed, but when she had come downstairs he hadn't been in the house. She had waited for a while, watching the T.V. in the living room, but by eleven o'clock he hadn't appeared, so she had gone to bed.

One last look at the blue boat to see if Carl would appear in the hatchway and then she moved away and began to dress. Some time today she would have to make up her mind whether to go with him when he left tomorrow or not. She had tried hard to come to a decision last night, but had failed. Mostly, she wanted to go, to cast aside caution and sail away with him, taking what came as he had suggested, elope with him as Liza had eloped with Greg.

'And look what happened to them,' she whispered to herself now. 'Do you want that to happen to you and Carl?'

She was afraid of commitment, she knew she was, because she was afraid the relationship wouldn't last. She was afraid that one day she would wake up far away in Peru and find out that Carl no longer wanted her to live with him. It might have been easier to decide if he had asked her to marry him, but he hadn't. He had just said, *'Come, fly with me to Peru.'*

The song she had heard sung so often by the bewitching sonorous voice of Frank Sinatra lilted through her mind. Many times, when she had heard it, she had longed to obey its invitation and fly away with someone she liked to visit the exotic places of the world. Now she had been invited to do that. But she didn't have the self-confidence to go. She was afraid of the consequences.

The morning was half over before she was able to talk to Greg, and then she had to invade the small room off the living room which he had decided to turn into a study, using an offer of coffee as a pretext to interrupt his absorption in a new book of psychology.

'Thanks,' he said with his charming smile as she

set down the mug. 'Where are the kids?'

'On the beach with Carl. They're clamming again.'

'They seemed to like him.' He leaned back in his chair and took a sip of coffee. 'You too?' he queried. 'Of course you do,' he added hastily. 'You wouldn't have gone sailing with him if you didn't. It's a good test of your ability to relate to another person, being cooped up with them on a small yacht,' he went on seriously.

'I had no choice but to go with him,' Margret put in quickly before he could digress into psychology.

'What do you mean?'

'Well, he was going to take Heather and Jamie with him whether I agreed to go or not, and I didn't think you would like them to go without me.' She looked round, found a chair and sat down. 'Are you going to tell me how the interviews went? Did you get a job?'

'I was offered two,' he said, laughing a little. 'A great boost for my ego to be offered two professorships! I've decided to accept the one offered by the local campus of the State University here because it will mean I can continue to live in this house. I can drive to the campus every day.'

'Will your aunt let you rent the house?' she asked.

'Carl seems to think she won't object. She doesn't come up here now and he won't be using it for the next couple of years. He's going back to Peru. He's been offered a senior position out there to look after his company's interests.'

'I'm glad you've got the position you wanted,' Margret said sincerely. 'I know how much it means to you, coming back to your own country.'

'You'll stay on with us, I hope, as housekeeper. The kids will be going to school come September, but I'll still need someone to look after them when they're at home and to do the general house-managing,' he said.

'I ... er ... there's something I have to tell you,' she replied quickly. 'I've a confession to make.'

'A confession?' Greg looked startled. 'What about? What have you done?'

'Deceived you.'

'In what way?'

'When I applied for this job I pretended to be older than I am. I did my hair like this and I didn't use make-up. I wore glasses that were only stage props. Mrs Kerridge of the agency said you wanted to employ an older woman, so I made myself look about thirty—at least I think I did.'

Greg went on staring at her, apparently stunned by her announcement.

'And I never guessed,' he said slowly at last. He leaned forward, a searching expression in his eyes. 'It was the glasses—they concealed a lot,' he murmured. He slumped back in his chair and ruffled his hair. 'But even so you would have thought I'd have. ...' He shook his head from side to side. 'I guess I was so desperate to get someone to look after Heather and Jamie that I never looked at you properly.' A wry smile curved his mouth. 'You know,

Margret, you didn't deceive me as much as I deceived myself. Something I've been pretty good at doing most of my life, to date.' Bitterness rasped in his voice. He paused and gave her a diffident glance. 'But it worked out for the best, didn't it? We've all got along well together and nothing awful has happened.'

'Until yesterday,' she said unhappily. 'I'll never forgive myself for not watching Jamie. If I'd been doing my job properly he wouldn't have fallen overboard.'

'Carl said it was as much his fault as yours—and you're not to let it be on your conscience. Jamie is alive and well, thanks to you. Surely you can see that?' he said earnestly.

'Yes. But I wasn't doing my job properly,' she argued stubbornly. 'Instead of keeping an eye on him I was. . . .' She broke off, feeling her face grow warm as she recalled what she had been doing; romanticising about Carl. 'I wasn't paying enough attention,' she added firmly.

'But accidents can happen any time to children even when we're watching them,' Greg insisted. 'And look at it this way. Falling in the water taught Jamie a lesson. It taught him that he has to watch out for himself instead of depending on other people to do that.' He sighed. 'Because he wasn't strong as a baby and infant and because Liza deserted him I've tended to cosset him, be over-protective,' he explained. 'But to get back to what we were discussing. You are going to stay with us, aren't you?'

At that point the extension telephone on the desk rang and as Greg reached out a hand for the receiver Margret rose to her feet.

'You are going to stay, aren't you?' he persisted, as the phone rang again.

'I ... I ... for the time being,' she said quickly, and left the room.

How could she leave? She had no other job and until Greg paid her her last month's wages she had no money. Unless she went with Carl she had to stay. A movement outside the living-room window caught her attention. Carl was stepping up on to the sun-deck, moving towards the front door with that predatory gracefulness, his wind-ruffled hair and sun-tanned skin glowing in the sunlight. He wouldn't be easy to live with, she thought. Every moment with him would be full of challenge. She would have to have her wits about her all the time. But she would never be bored with him.

'Have you talked to Greg today? Have you told him about your deception of him?'

He was there suddenly in the room behind her, big, blond and vibrant.

'Yes, I have, the confession has been made,' she replied lightly, turning to him.

'And?' Coldly blue, his glance swept curiously over her.

'He seemed to think he deceived himself and he wants me to stay on here to look after the children and keep house.'

'So?' His eyes narrowed speculatively.

'I've decided to stay . . . for the time being,' she said coolly. 'After all, I have no choice at the moment. I can't afford to fly back to England and I don't have another job to go to.'

'You have a choice,' Carl retorted. 'And you know damn well what it is. You can come to Peru with me.'

'To do what?' she flared. 'To be your mistress?'

His mouth twisted and his lashes covered the expression in his eyes as he looked down at the floor.

'You could put it like that, yes,' he replied. He stepped closer. 'Margret, this is the last time I'll ask you. Will you come away with me tomorrow?'

'I . . . oh, I don't think I can,' she whispered wildly, just as Heather came bouncing into the room.

'Carl, let's go now and sell the clams,' the girl demanded, coming up to him and, taking hold of his hand, began to pull him towards the study. 'Come and ask Daddy to drive us to Roskeag in his car.'

Carl's muttered imprecation was unprintable and he gave Margret an icy glance before turning away and going with the girl.

'Margret, I've cut my finger on a shell!' Jamie's voice wailed as he came in banging the screen door behind him. 'Look, it's bleeding!' He held out a grubby forefinger on which a speck of blood was showing. 'I want a plaster on it.'

Subduing the emotions the short encounter with Carl had churned up, Margret took Jamie to the kitchen, washed the hurt finger and applied a Band-aid. Happy again, he went off to see Greg too. Lingering in the kitchen, she listened to the voices of the children and the two men as they all crossed the living room. Footsteps came towards the kitchen and Greg put his head round the doorway.

'We're off to Roskeag. We'll call in at the Spencers' on our way. Want to come?' he asked.

'No, thanks. I've a pile of washing to do.'

'Okay. See you later.'

The afternoon was well advanced and Margret was taking in the washing she had pegged out earlier to blow in the wind and the sun when Brett strolled out of the lane.

'I thought you might be on your own,' he said in his cheerful way, 'so I came over to say goodbye. I'm off tomorrow, going climbing with some friends, and after that I'll be going straight back to college. How did the cruise go?'

'Very well, thank you. I enjoyed seeing some of the islands,' she replied, lifting the laundry basket into which she had put the clothes and moving towards the house.

'Too bad you couldn't have stayed away longer,' he drawled, holding the back door open for her and following her into the kitchen.

'Why?'

'Laura was really enjoying having Greg to herself. You should have been here to see their first meeting after ten years when Greg turned up on Thursday!'

'He came on Thursday?' exclaimed Margret, putting the laundry basket down on the table. 'But he wasn't expected until Friday. If I'd thought he would be here Thursday I'd never have let the children go with Carl and I wouldn't have gone either. He must have been very puzzled when we weren't here.'

'Well, if he was, he didn't show it. And he didn't have time to miss you at all, Laura was over here most of the time making meals for both of them, going for walks with him.' Brett gave her an under-browed glance. 'What's going to happen to you now that Greg has got fixed up with a job at the local university campus? Are you going to stay on?'

'He's asked me to, but I haven't decided yet,' she said coolly.

'This place is okay now, in the summer,' said Brett, leaning casually against the table. 'And it isn't half bad in the fall. But come winter!' He shuddered a little. 'It can be cold and it's really remote. I guess you might find it hard to live here, not being born to it and having no friends or relatives here to call on.'

'Are you trying to put me off?' she asked, laughing.

'No, just pointing out the reality of the situation. It would be different, now, if you were married to Greg and were making a home for both of you.'

'Perhaps he'll ask your sister to marry him now they've met up again,' she said lightly, sorting the clothes into one pile for Heather and one for Jamie.

'Not while you're here, he won't,' said Brett. 'He won't see the need to get married while someone like you is here to look after hearth and home. Greg will have to be in the situation of being a single parent who can't cope before he'll think of asking Laura to marry him.' He moved away from the table. 'Guess I'd better be pushing off,' he said with his friendly grin, holding out his hand. 'I enjoyed our visit to the theatre together, and I'm sorry there wasn't time for us to go to one of the other summer theatres.'

He left, and Margret continued with her work of sorting out clothing and putting it away in the appropriate drawers and closets, and all the time her thoughts were busy with what Brett had told her. His remarks about Greg and Laura recalled to mind Carl's jeers about his cousin and she recognised them as being a true assessment of her employer. While she was there doing everything a wife would normally do Greg wouldn't think of marrying again, especially since he had had such a bad experience with Liza.

It was almost five-thirty when Greg eventually returned with the children, without Carl and without Laura. Margret served the evening meal and afterwards they all went for a walk along the shore. When the children had gone to bed and the last of the sunset stained the western sky with one single band of crimson light against which the islands were silhouetted in black, Greg called Margret into the small study-like room and handed her a cheque.

'That's what I owe you for the last few weeks,' he said. 'Have I got it right?'

'Yes, thanks.' She glanced down at the amount he had written. 'Greg, what happens next? Do you start work at the campus soon?'

'No. I reckon I can have two weeks off,' he said, leaning back in his chair. 'Tomorrow Laura is going to take the kids over to the fair at Midworth.'

'She seems to like them and they like her,' Margret said slowly and thoughtfully. 'It's a pity. . . .' She broke off deliberately, biting her lip.

'What's the pity?' he asked, his interest caught by her hesitation as she had hoped it would be.

'It isn't really any of my business,' she continued, 'but I can't help thinking what a good mother Miss Spencer would be for Heather and Jamie, or for any other children.'

'I agree with you,' he said enthusiastically. 'She would.'

'Then why don't you ask her to marry you?'

His eyes flickered with surprise at her frankness. Then he shook his head slowly and smiled at her rather pityingly as if she were totally devoid of understanding.

'She wouldn't have me,' he said.

'What makes you think that?'

'She has a very good job with a school board and she's in love with Carl. She's always been in love with him, and that was why. . . .' He paused, an expression of bitterness flitting across his face.

Standing up, he jammed his hands in his trouser pockets and paced away to the window to look out at the encroaching darkness. 'I wanted to marry Laura years ago, when we were still at college,' he muttered. 'But I knew she loved Carl and was waiting for him to return from Vietnam. She was so hurt when he came with Liza in tow, I had to do something about it. I thought that if I took Liza away with me Carl would see how much Laura loved him.'

There was a short silence. Greg turned to look at her and his brief laugh was dreary.

'I made a mistake. Carl didn't react the way I hoped he would. He went away too and . . . well . . . Liza insisted I marry her.'

Margret was hardly able to believe her ears. The tangle of ten years ago had been even more complicated than Brett had suggested.

'Are you telling me that you asked Liza to go away with you because you wanted to help Laura, because you loved Laura although you knew she loved Carl?' she asked.

'Quixotic of me, wasn't it?' His slight smile mocked himself. 'I loved Laura. I think I'm still a little in love with her. But Carl will always come first with her. Tonight they've gone out together and I know she's hoping he'll ask her to go with him to Peru.'

'But supposing he doesn't ask her? Suppose he asks another woman to go with him?' Margret asked. 'Surely Laura will get the message then, that he doesn't love her?'

'She might,' he admitted grudgingly. 'But who would he ask? There isn't another woman in his life right now. He'd have brought her with him if there was.'

A car stopped outside the house. Doors slammed and footsteps clumped across the sun-deck. The front door opened. Laura's voice sounded clearly and was answered by Carl's.

'I think I'll go to bed,' said Margret. 'Goodnight.'

She passed Laura and Carl as they came through the living room. Laura smiled at her brightly. She seemed to be in high spirits. Carl ignored her completely and the two of them went into the room where Greg was sitting.

In her bedroom Margret looked out of the window. The night was dark, but not as dark as the night Carl had come. Stars glimmered in the blue-black sky and their shine was reflected here and there in the equally blue-black water.

Turning away, she switched on the bedside lamp and sat down on the edge of the bed to stare at the cheque Greg had given to her. When it was cashed she would have enough money to cover her air fare to England and some over. Now that she had been paid she could leave.

Come, fly with me. The words of the song lilted through her mind again. This morning Carl had asked her to go with him for the last time and she had refused. Had he asked Laura this evening as Greg had suggested he would? Was that why Laura had been so lighthearted when she had entered the house just now?

Margret's fingers curled tightly over the edge of the cheque. She couldn't let Carl take Laura away from Greg in the way Greg had taken Liza away ten years ago. And there was only one way to stop that from happening. She would have to go with Carl herself, remove herself and him from the scene, here at Lindley's Point, so that Laura and Greg could act out their love affair without interference and without the distraction of alternatives.

She sat for a long time listening. At last she heard sounds of people moving about coming from downstairs. Tiptoeing along the landing, she looked down. Light glimmered on Laura's bright head as she said something to Greg, while Carl leaned casually in the archway leading to the living room. Greg went out with Laura, accompanying her to her car and, after a few moments, Margret went down the stairs and followed Carl as he went into the living room.

'Carl?'

'Mmm?' He swung round to face her.

'I've changed my mind. I'd like to go with you, when you leave.'

He stared at her narrowly for a few seconds.

'All the way? As I suggested?' he asked. 'Fly to Peru and live with me there?'

'Yes.'

'Why?'

The abrupt question stumped her for a moment and so did the suspicion so clearly expressed on his face.

'I . . . I . . . can't bear the idea of you going away without me,' she admitted in a rush, and her voice wobbled convincingly.

He frowned and stepped towards her. Fingers under her chin, he tilted her face towards the light so he could search it with hard cold eyes.

'Is this an act?' he purred menacingly.

'No, no. I really want to go when you go,' she insisted.

'What about Greg? Have you told him that you've decided to leave?'

'Not yet. I had to speak to you first, make sure that. . . .'

'*I* hadn't changed my mind,' Carl finished for her, releasing her and half turning away from her. 'Well, I haven't. But if you really want to come you'll come tonight and sleep on the boat. I want to set sail early in the morning to catch the flood tide along the Reach.' He faced her again, his face tough and unyielding. 'So if you're coming, go pack your clothes now and tell Greg you're leaving. Meet me on the shore by the dinghy in twenty minutes. I'll be waiting for you.'

He wasn't responding as she had expected him to respond to her change of mind. He wasn't exactly ecstatic, she thought ruefully as she packed her clothes into her two cases, thankful that she didn't have much to pack. She changed into jeans, a shirt and a warm sweater. Making sure she had Greg's cheque, her passport and other credentials in her handbag, she slung it over her shoulder and left the room, wondering what she would say to Greg.

Leaving her cases in the hallway, she went to the study, but although the light was still on Greg wasn't there. He wasn't in the kitchen either, yet she was sure she had heard him enter the house while she had been packing. She looked at her watch. Her twenty minutes were almost up. Sitting down at the desk in the study, she found paper and pen, scrawled a note for Greg explaining where she had gone, with whom and why, and signed her name.

She left the house quickly and quietly and walked down to the shore. Carl was there, a dark shape beside the dark bulk of the dinghy. In a few minutes she was sitting in the stern as he rowed swiftly across the smooth water towards the yacht.

Once on board he ordered her to get some sleep and she went to the forward cabin where she had slept with Heather. She slept heavily and was wakened by the throb of the engine and the sound of the anchor being pulled up. Pearly-grey dawn light filtered through the porthole. Rolling out of the bunk, she dressed quickly and arrived in the cockpit just in time to see the house at Lindley's Point dis-

appear behind the reef of rust-pink rocks. It was like
the closing scene in a play about her life, she
thought. The time with Greg and the children was
over and fast becoming a memory. The voyage with
Carl would be an interval, a brief respite before the
curtains opened at the start of the next act.

Along the wide reach of water separating Deer
Island from the mainland they sailed with the sun
coming up behind them, gilding the sails, changing
everything that was grey on land and sea to green,
yellow, brown and blue. The wind was strong but
free and the yacht surged forward, spray flying over
its bow. Under the curving arch and delicate steel
webbing of a suspension bridge connecting the
island to the mainland, they sailed into the western
part of the reach, towards the tiny rocky Pumpkin
Island, with its old lighthouse standing guard over
the entrance to Penobscot Bay.

On the blue luminosity of the bay islands floated,
humpbacked, spiky with spruce trees, edged with
tawny rocks and yellow beaches and in the distance,
lavender blue, the Camden Hills were etched
sharply against the sun-drenched sky. The sheets
were pulled in. The sails were tautened. The yacht
heeled over and the wind sang in the rigging. Across
glittering waves the boat leapt and plunged towards
the end of a long island.

After another sea-soaked, sun-sparkling hour of
sailing they reached the dark spruce-covered penin-
sula and turning eased the sheets to free the sails.

Suddenly they were in sheltered water, smooth and shadowed. Sliding silently, the wind behind it, the boat moved along a narrow channel between rock-strewn sandy shores.

It was a short cut, Carl explained, one he had sailed many times with his uncle when he had been a boy, and it could only be used when the tide was full. From the narrowness of the channel they turned into a wide bay where grey seals sunbathed on rocky islets. raising sleek heads to glance at the boat as it passed. Huge houses, half hidden among trees, were built on the shores of the bay—the summer residences, Carl said, of wealthy people from New York and other cities.

Leaving the bay, they burst out into the sunlit sea and there across the water white houses and a church steeple gleamed against the thick summer greenness of a hill, the town of Camden. The interval between the acts was almost over, thought Margret regretfully, for she had enjoyed every minute of the exhilarating five-hour sail. Now she understood why so many people went sailing. While on the sea the problems she associated with living on the land were forgotten. Soon she would have to brace herself, pre-pare for the part she was going to play when she was on the shore again.

They berthed the yacht at the yacht club wharf where Carl's friend Paul Munsen was waiting with his wife and some other friends.

'Looks like you've had a good cruise,' said Paul,

glancing curiously at Margret as she stepped on the wharf, and the other people who were standing about laughed.

'Seems to me you were all alone when you left here, Carl, a week ago,' drawled a mocking male voice. 'Is she a stowaway, or did you find her ship-wrecked on one of the deserted islands out there on the bay?'

'This is Margret,' Carl replied easily, not at all perturbed by their mockery, and he introduced them to her in the same way, not bothering with last names.

They were all very pleasant and friendly, but Margret could not help feeling they regarded her as Carl's latest affair and she was glad when at last, after they had eaten a sandwich lunch, he guided her over to the car in which he had driven from Boston the previous week.

The drive to Boston in the hot afternoon sunlight was mostly silent and by the time they were approaching the New Hampshire and Massachusetts border Margret was feeling on edge. Ever since last night when she had told him she had changed her mind she had sensed a difference in Carl, a sort of withdrawal. Several times she had tried to start a conversation with him, but his response had been curt to the point of rudeness.

Was he regretting having asked her to go with him to Peru? Or was it a case of having got his own way at last he felt he didn't have to make any more

effort to attract her? So many times during the past
few days she had felt close to him. But now, sitting
in the front of the car beside him as it hurtled along
a wide highway, they were two strangers with
nothing to say to each other, yet intending to fly
together to another country and to live there together in the same apartment or house, sharing bed
and board.

Revulsion of feeling surged up inside her like
sickness as she recalled how Carl's friends in
Camden had looked at her with sly smirks on their
faces, drawing their own conclusions about the relationship between Carl and herself. She imagined
other meetings with other friends of his wherever she
might go with him. Always it would be like that, the
sidelong knowing looks, the half-hidden grins. Never
would there be any respect, any openness, even in
this age of permissiveness.

She had been crazy to agree to go with him. No,
not really, she argued with herself immediately. She
had come with him for a good reason. She had removed herself from the scene at Lindley's Point. But
she didn't have to stay with him. She didn't have to
go all the way. When she reached Boston she could
leave him, find a place to stay the night, and tomorrow she would cash her cheque and buy a ticket to
England. Yes, that was what she would do.

The opportunity to part company with him came
before they reached Boston when he stopped at a
service station in an old town called Salem to fill up

the car's tank with petrol. Noting that there was a rest room, glad that she had packed her overnight things in her big shoulder bag, Margret got out of the car and went towards the room. She stayed inside for a while. When she came out again she looked cautiously round the corner of the building. Carl had his back to her and was talking to the station attendant. Turning, she hurried to the back of the building and ran across the parking lot at the back, towards another street at right angles to the one along which they had been driving when they had stopped.

It was beginning to rain, a soft stealthy drizzle which had come with dusk, smearing the sidewalks and blurring the lights which twinkled out from a concrete building that loomed up ahead of her. Across the front of the building was a sign announcing that it was a motel. Without hesitation Margret pushed open one of the swing glass doors of the entrance to the building and stepped into the carpeted foyer, where soft music played.

There was another person at the reception desk registering, so she had to wait for a few minutes. At last her turn came and she asked for a room. The receptionist, a severe-looking woman, eyed her up and down.

'Do you have any credit?' she snapped suspiciously.

'Credit?' Margret queried.

'Sure. Do you have a credit card? Or are you going to pay cash for the room right now?'

'You mean I have to pay for the room before I can have it?'

'That's right, ma'am.'

'How much?'

The woman told her the price of a single room and dismay hit Margret like a chill. She knew she didn't have that much cash on her.

'I don't have a credit card and I don't have enough cash to pay now,' she explained. 'But I do have a cheque made out to me by my employer. Couldn't you take it and take payment for the room out of it and give me the change if I endorse it?'

The woman shook her head. She looked as if she didn't care and didn't want to help.

'Can't do that,' she said abruptly, and looked past Margret to someone who was standing behind her. 'Can I help you sir?' she asked.

'Not right now. I'm waiting for this lady.' Carl's voice was quiet and smooth, too quiet and smooth for Margret's liking. She turned and faced him.

'How did you know I'd come here?' she quavered, her heart sinking when she saw the set of his jaw and the acid blue glare of his eyes.

'When you didn't come back to the car I went round to the rest room to check you were all right and I saw you loping across the yard at the back of the station. I went back to the car and drove down this street, saw you come in here. Why the hell did you take off like that, without saying anything? What were you trying to do?'

Margret didn't answer. Turning, she made for the

doors. She didn't get very far before she felt his hand
on her arm. He swung her round to face him.

'You're not going anywhere until you've told me
what you have in mind,' he snarled softly.

'We can't talk here,' she said, glaring at him.
'Someone is listening.'

His glance slid to the receptionist, who was leaning on her desk watching them with avid curiosity,
and his grip on Margret's arm slackened temporarily. Taking advantage of his distraction, she dived
towards the swing doors, which opened quickly and
obligingly. She ran out into the street and along the
sidewalk.

Carl caught up with her at a crossroads where she
had to wait for lights to change and his hand
gripped her arm again. Both breathing hard, they
stared at each other in the lamplit drizzle.

'That was a neat little trick,' he said. 'But you're
not going to get away from me without an explana-
tion. What were you doing in that motel?'

'I was going to spend the night there. Carl, I
can't go with you to Peru. I'm going back to England,' she replied woodenly. The rain, although soft,
was very wet, soaking their hair and streaming
down their faces.

'I had a feeling you had something like this in
mind when you came to me last night and said
you'd changed your mind,' Carl's voice rasped. He
gave her a rough little shake. 'But I didn't think
you'd run out on me without telling me you were

going. Hadn't it occurred to you I might be worried, wondering where the hell you'd gone? It isn't always safe for someone like you to be alone on the streets at night.'

'I thought you'd be relieved,' she muttered.

'Relieved?' he exclaimed. 'Why should I feel relieved, for God's sake?'

'I . . . I . . . could tell on the way here that you're having regrets about asking me to go away with you.'

'A mind-reader, eh?' he scoffed. 'Well, you're wrong. I don't go in for regrets and having brought you so far I'm not letting you go . . . yet. You'll stay tonight in Boston, at the Lindley House there, with my aunt Marion, and maybe tomorrow, when you're less tired, we'll discuss what you'll do next. I might even cash that cheque for you at my bank.'

'But I . . . I . . . can't go and stay with your aunt,' she argued.

'Why not?'

'Well . . . what will she think?' she mumbled. 'About us . . . about you and me?'

'She'll think just what Paul and the others thought back in Camden,' he replied tauntingly. 'She'll think we're having an affair.'

'But I don't want her or anyone else to think that!' she complained.

'Then why did you come away with me?' he demanded, and his grip on her arm tightened. Through the drizzle she looked up. His face was half lit by the street lamps, half hidden in the shadow, a mask hiding what he was feeling or thinking. 'Why didn't you stay with Greg?' he persisted. 'Did you find out about him and Laura?'

'Yes, I did,' she replied, surprise lilting in her voice.

'I see.' His mouth twisted cynically and he put the back of his free hand across one cheek to wipe away raindrops. 'I think that perhaps I understand now why you've come with me,' he added, letting go of her arm and half turning away as if he intended to walk back to the car and leave her standing there. But he didn't go. Instead he swung back.

'You're still welcome to come on to Boston with me,' he said flatly. 'You'll be better off staying in my aunt's house than in some crummy motel, even if you can find one that will let you have a room without asking for payment first.'

'All right, I'll come to Boston,' she whispered. She was only giving in, she told herself, because she was tired, damp and hungry and had no strength left to fight him any more.

Through the wet darkness spangled with thousands of lights they drove towards the city, turning off the highway at last to twist and turn among the narrow streets of the old part until they came to a tall narrow house which was wedged between other tall narrow houses on a steep sloping street. Old-fashioned street lamps cast a soft glow on mellow red

brick, arched doorways and sash windows framed by
painted shutters. The whole area expressed a discreet affluence.

Carl parked the car at the kerb in front of the
house, got out and came round to open the door on
Margret's side.

'It's late, but I don't think Aunt Marion will have
gone to bed yet,' he said as with a hand beneath her
elbow he guided her up some shallow steps and
pressed a lighted bell push beside the beautifully
panelled black-painted front door, which was set
under a spider-web fanlight through which light
glowed faintly. Listening to the bell peal musically
inside the house, Margret felt nerves in her stomach
twinge.

'Carl,' she muttered, turning to him, 'I can't. . . .'
Somehow she was in his arms, being held closely.
His nylon sailing jacket was wet beneath her cheek
and she felt his fingers at her temple, stroking back
wet tails of hair.

'It'll be okay,' he murmured. 'Right now you're
tired and confused. A meal, a night's rest in a comfortable bed will do all the good in the world and
tomorrow everything will look brighter and better.
You'll get over it.'

Light from an overhead porch lamp streamed
down on them suddenly and the door opened.
Keeping one arm about her, Carl turned to face the
slim white-haired woman who stood in the doorway
staring at them in amazement.

'Well, you're the last person I expected to see tonight, Carl,' she said in a sweet tinkling voice. 'Greg has just called. He wanted to know if I knew when you're flying to Peru. He seemed to be very concerned about someone called Margret.' Her bright birdlike eyes swerved to Margret. 'I guess you're Margret,' she added. 'Greg seems to think you've eloped with Carl.' She looked back at Carl and frowned almost severely as if displeased with him. 'The poor girl looks exhausted,' she rebuked him. 'You'd best come in and explain what you've been up to now.'

They went into the house. Margret had an impression of a long narrow hall with a high ceiling, of mirrors on walls reflecting all of them, of highly polished hall furniture.

'I guess you'd like something to eat,' said Marion Lindley, leading the way along the hall into a brightly lit modern kitchen where copper pans gleamed against wooden panelling. 'If I know you, Carl, you haven't stopped on the drive down to feed Margret.'

'You know me,' he retorted equably.

They sat at a round table made from maple wood on matching ladderbacked chairs and ate a delicious seafood and cheese concoction which Marion Lindley took from a freezer and heated in a micro-wave oven.

'So, is it true?' she asked, sitting down at the table with them after she had poured coffee for them. 'Have you eloped with this ruffian, Margret?'

'Not really,' Margret muttered.

'I asked Margret if she would like to come with me when I left Lindley's Point yesterday and she decided she would,' put in Carl quietly. 'So here we are.'

'And that's all there is to it?' exclaimed Mrs Lindley, arching her eyebrows at Margret.

'That's all there is to it,' Carl replied firmly.

'Then I'm sure I don't understand why Greg was in such a state. To hear him you'd have thought the end of the world had come just because Margret had left Lindley's Point!'

'It might seem like that to him for a while,' said Carl, his mouth curling sardonically. 'You see, Margret has been his housekeeper and has looked after Heather and Jamie for the past year and a half, so he must be wondering what's hit him since she left.'

'But isn't there anyone to take your place?' Mrs Lindley asked anxiously, looking at Margret again, her head tilted to one side in that strange birdlike way.

'No,' said Margret, shaking her head.

'Sure there's someone to take her place,' Carl's voice overrode her whispered answer. 'If only we could get Greg to see further than the end of his nose. Laura Spencer is staying at the Spencer place.'

'Is she? I always liked Laura,' said Mrs Lindley warmly. 'At one time I thought she and Greg might marry, but that was before Liza came on the scene.' She sighed sadly, then brightened again. 'I'm glad

Greg and Laura have met again. I hope something comes of it.'

'That's exactly what I was thinking,' said Carl. Pushing back his chair, he rose to his feet. 'Why don't you show Margret the room where she's going to sleep tonight,' he added. 'She didn't have much sleep last night and has been going all day. I'll give Greg a call now and tell him she's okay and is staying here.'

He strode from the room, and at once Mrs Lindley turned to look at Margret again.

'You're from England, aren't you?' she said. 'What part?'

'From Surrey, not far from London.' Now that she had eaten and was feeling comfortable Margret was having difficulty in keeping her eyes open.

'Cynthia came from England too,' Mrs Lindley chattered.

'Cynthia?' Margret did her best to smother a yawn.

'Carl's mother. His father, who was my husband's twin brother, met her when he was in England studying for a post-graduate degree at Cambridge. Edwin was an engineer too, like Carl.' She looked at Margret closely again. 'Do you mean to tell me he hasn't told you about his parents?'

'No. He . . . we . . . I haven't known him for very long, only a week, Mrs Lindley, I. . . .'

'Call me Aunt Marion, dear. Everyone does,' said the little woman, getting to her feet. 'You're looking really washed out and just a little forlorn as if you, like Greg, don't know what's hit you. Are you sure you've done the right thing in leaving his employment? I hope Carl hasn't been too overbearing. He has a tendency to behave something like a bulldozer at times. If he thinks someone is in the way he'll scoop them up and remove them. He's very like my husband Earl, a managing sort of person. His intentions are often good, but the methods he uses are often a little rough.'

'I'm quite sure I had to leave,' Margret replied dully, and rubbed at her eyes. 'Mrs ... Aunt Marion, I would really like to go to bed, if you don't mind.'

'Of course you would. Come along then. I'll take you upstairs now and show you to the guest room. You can have a hot bath, if you like, before you go to bed.'

Grateful for Aunt Marion's placid acceptance of her, vaguely aware that something was wrong between herself and Carl and yet unable to make out what it was, Margret had the hot bath and climbed into a wide bed in the pleasant guest room. At once waves of fatigue washed over her and dragged her down at last into the warm, dark oblivion of sleep.

CHAPTER FIVE

TEN hours later Margret awoke to the throb of heavy traffic moving through the streets of the city not far from the house. For a while she wondered sleepily where she was. Opening her eyes, she looked round a pleasant high-ceilinged room into which sunlight was shining through frilled net curtains.

The walls of the room were painted sage green and the curtains and bedcover were made from silver and green brocade. A thick camel-coloured carpet covered the floor from wall to wall and maple furniture gleamed with a golden sheen. In a big mirror on the dressing table, which was set between the two sash windows, she could see herself reflected, lying in the bed her dark hair streaming across a plump lace-edged pillow.

She stretched luxuriously, feeling the silky cotton of expensive sheets sliding against her bare legs. She had slept well and felt thoroughly rested. Now she was much more able to cope with the situation in which she found herself, as Carl had suggested she would be after a night's rest.

You'll get over it, he had said. Get over what? Get over leaving Greg's employment? Or get over the realisation that she had fallen in love with Carl?

Throwing back the bedclothes, she slid off the bed

and went to the windows. Through the curtains she looked down into a narrow street paved with cobble-stones, relics of the time when the old city of Boston had been built. Red brick houses sloped down either side of the street, all joined together, elegant in their simplicity. Her mind drifted back to the previous evening when she and Carl had stood on the steps of this house waiting for the door to open. He had been surprisingly gentle, but to recall his understanding then, the warm strength of his arm around her, was to follow a dangerous path. If she dwelt on his good qualities she would never be able to drag herself away from him. She must keep in the forefront of her mind that she had only come away with him to help Greg and today she must cash her cheque, get money to buy an airline ticket so she could leave as soon as she could.

She found her shoulder bag and took out her wallet. The cheque wasn't in it. Frantically she searched her bag, throwing everything out of it on to the bed. The cheque wasn't in it at all. Hand to her head, she racked her memory, trying to recall what she had done with the cheque after showing it to the receptionist at the hotel. It had been in her hand when Carl had spoken to the receptionist. It had been in her hand when she had run towards the swing doors and out into the street. Or had it?

Groaning, she sank down on the edge of the bed, staring at the empty wallet, acknowledging mis-erably that she must have dropped the cheque when she had raced away from Carl. She had lost it, and now she had no money at all.

A knock on the door startled her. Going over to the door, she opened it. Marion Lindley, dressed in a neat suit of blue knit, her fluffy white hair like a halo round her head, her blue-grey eyes twinkling, stood outside holding a small tray on which there was a coffee pot, cream jug and sugar bowl, a cup and saucer and a plate of muffins.

'Good, you're up,' she said, stepping into the room. 'I thought you'd like to have your breakfast in peace, up here—take your time over it,' she added, setting the tray down on the bedside table.

'Thank you. It's kind of you,' said Margret. 'I'm afraid I must have overslept. What time is it, please?'

'Quarter after ten. But you're not to worry about that. Carl and I decided it would be best if you slept in and took it easy today.' Marion tilted her head to one side. 'You're looking much better.'

'I'm feeling better.'

'Now, I have to go out this morning, to a committee meeting—I do a lot of voluntary work—otherwise I'd love to stay and talk with you. But I'll be back for lunch. Please make yourself comfortable. You can stay here as long as you like. Carl has gone to the head offices of his company which are in Philadelphia. He says he won't be back until Friday.' Marion went towards the door. 'Pauline, my housekeeper, will be working about the house so if you need anything, just ask her. I'll see you later.'

Marion left the room and Margret poured coffee for herself. She took one of the hot buttered blueberry muffins and bit into it. Soft and spongy, it melted in the mouth, so she took another and carrying her coffee cup over to the window looked down into the narrow street where Marion Lindley was getting into the back seat of a sleek grey car, the door of which was being held open by a chauffeur.

So Carl had gone to Philadelphia and wouldn't be back until Friday. He had gone without telling her he was going, without saying goodbye and without leaving a message for her. Not that he had to tell her anything, she thought hastily, suppressing the feeling of rejection that welled up inside her. They were both free agents. She was free to do what she wanted to do and he was free to do what he wanted to do. By going away and staying away for the next few days he was indicating that he had accepted her decision not to fly with him to Peru. He wasn't going to ask her again and he had left the door wide open for her to leave and go back to England.

But without money she couldn't go anywhere. Without money she was virtually a prisoner in this house. Frowning worriedly, she went back to the tray and poured more coffee. Supposing someone had picked up the cheque and had attempted to cash it? Shouldn't she inform Greg of her loss so he could stop the cheque before it could be cashed?

She finished her coffee, washed and dressed quickly and went downstairs, taking the breakfast tray to the kitchen. She asked the plump grey-haired woman who was the housekeeper if there was a phone she could use and was directed to the writing room, a small panelled room near the front door which was furnished with an antique writing table and several chairs. Sitting down, she dialled directly through to the house at Lindley's Point and listened to the phone ringing there for about six times before she set down the receiver. Greg must have gone out and she would have to try later.

Marion returned, as she had promised, for lunch and they were eating in the dining room when the front door bell rang. Pauline went to answer the door and in a few seconds Greg appeared in the dining room.

'Greg, how nice to see you!' Aunt Marion exclaimed, rising to her feet and going across to greet him.

'Nice to see you, too, Aunt Marion.' He kissed her cheek.

'We're just finishing lunch. Perhaps you'll have some. Pauline, bring another plate and a knife and fork. Are the children with you, Greg?'

'No. I left them with Laura. You remember Laura Spencer? She said she'd look after them so I could come here and do some studying in the Athenaeum,' he said, following his aunt across the room to the table.

His hair was a wild tangle, he hadn't shaved and his eyes were slightly bloodshot from driving. He had obviously chained-smoked all the way from

Lindley's Point to Boston, because he reeked of tobacco smoke and fine grey tobacco ash was scattered across the lapels of his brown corduroy jacket.

'Thank God you're still here,' he muttered, his dark eyes expressing his bewilderment and anxiety. 'Where's Carl?'

'He's in Philadelphia,' Marion answered calmly. Standing in the doorway of the room, she looked from Greg to Margret and back to Greg again. 'I can see you two have a lot to say to each other, so I'm going to get out of your way,' she added. 'Will you be staying the night, Greg?'

'No, thanks, Aunt Marion. I'll stay with the parents while I'm down here. They were away when I came back from England.'

Marion nodded, looked across at Margret again and to Margret's surprise winked, as if she found Greg's behaviour amusing. Then she went sedately from the room and Pauline came in with dishes for Greg and a fresh pot of coffee.

'Why did you go off like that, without any warning?' Greg asked as he heaped his plate with salad from the big wooden bowl. 'I would never have believed you could do anything so crazy and irresponsible!'

'I did warn you. Or at least I tried to,' Margret retorted. 'I tried to tell you I didn't want to stay and work for you much longer, but you wouldn't listen. You kept insisting that you needed me and depended on me. . . .'

'But I did and I do depend on you,' he replied.

'Well, you shouldn't,' she snapped, saw hurt flicker across his face and bit her lip. 'Oh, Greg, please try to understand. It was best for you if I came away with Carl. You shouldn't have come after me. Why have you?'

'To stop you going away with him to Peru, of course. You mustn't go with him, and there's only one way I can think of to stop you.' He braced his shoulders and looked directly at her, his face very serious. 'Margret, will you marry me?'

She was so unprepared she gasped and blinked, then stared at him.

'What did you say?' she croaked at last.

'I asked you to marry me,' he replied. 'I should have thought about it before, but I've had a lot on my mind lately trying to find a job. I'd probably have got round to it later on this year, once we were settled. I should have asked you the other night, when we were talking about the future. If we get married it will solve everything. . . .'

'No, it won't!' Margret spoke sharply to stop him and he looked up from his plate of salad to stare at her in surprise. 'You got married once before for the same reason. You asked Liza to marry you to solve a problem, and look what happened. She was unhappy and you were unhappy.' The expression of pain flitted across his face again and she leaned forward urgently. 'Please try to understand, Greg. I like you, but I don't want to marry you, so the answer is no. If you want to marry again, ask Laura.'

'I've told you, she won't have me. She's still in love with Carl,' he muttered. 'She was hoping he would ask her to go to Peru with him, but instead he asked you.' He rumpled his hair with his fingers. 'I don't understand why he did ask you to go away with him. But then I never could understand Carl. He doesn't follow any predictable pattern.' He looked across the table at her again. 'Margret, you'll be much safer if you marry me than if you go away with him. He isn't the marrying kind and. . . .'

'I don't want to be another Liza,' she said coldly.

'What do you mean?' he demanded. 'Surely you don't think that I'm asking you to marry me because you're like her? You're nothing like Liza.'

'Not in looks or ways, perhaps, but living at Lindley's Point in the same house as you I must seem like Liza to Laura. That was why I left, Greg, so you would ask Laura to marry you. Oh, can't you see? Laura would like to be your wife. She would like to mother Heather and Jamie. You shouldn't be here. You should be in Maine, with Laura.'

'I wish I could believe you're right,' he sighed, shaking his head from side to side. 'But I can't. While Laura believes Carl isn't married she'll always hope that one day he'll ask her, and she'll never marry me.'

Margret stared at him in exasperation. For a highly-qualified, well-educated man he was remarkably blind. But then wasn't it acknowledged that people who were psychologists or psychiatrists were notoriously bad at solving their own problems and often lacked the basic common sense of more simple, less educated people? She had a great urge to take hold of Greg's shoulders and give him a good shake to wake him up to the reality of the situation. There must be something she could do or say to convince she was right. Almost at once the way came to her, a flash of light illuminating her mind, and she went into action.

'Carl won't be unmarried for much longer,' she said coolly and steadily. 'He and I are going to be married here in Boston before we go to Peru.'

To say Greg was astonished by her announcement was to make the understatement of the year, she thought wryly, and she wouldn't have been at all surprised if he told her he didn't believe her. Somehow she had to put on an act to make him believe her.

'I know it seems incredible,' she went on, looking down at her hands and smiling what she hoped was a mysterious smile, hinting that she and Carl had secrets. 'It still seems that way to me because it happened so suddenly.'

'But you've only known him for a week,' Greg said weakly.

'I know. But we hit it off straight away. And then, while we were cruising with the children, we got to know one another rather well.' Again she smiled, hinting at untold intimacies. 'I would have liked to have told you before I left Lindley's Point, but we didn't really decide to get married, until we arrived in Boston. We're going to make the announcement as soon as Carl comes back from Philadephia on Friday. So you see you can go back to Maine and tell Laura. . . .'

'My God, you and Carl!' he interrupted her. 'I would never have thought that someone as delicate and as elusive as you are would fall for a tough, trouble-shooting guy like Carl.' He glanced at her, doubt expressed in his eyes. 'Margret, are you sure?'

'I'm sure,' she said, still steady.

'My God,' he muttered again, raking a hand through his hair. 'You'll have to forgive me for finding it very hard to believe. In fact I won't believe it until I see it happen, and I'm not going back to Maine until I have seen it happen. I'm going to stay right here in Boston and see it happen. I'm going to be Carl's best man.'

'Oh, but . . .' Margret's thoughts raced in panic, 'what about the children? Supposing Laura can't look after them for longer than two days?'

'She can bring them here and be at the wedding ceremony too and maybe then she'll be convinced at last that Carl doesn't love her. Yeah, that's what I'll do. I'll call her tonight and tell her to drive down with them so that we can all be there when you and Carl get married.' His dark face was alight suddenly and his brown eyes smiled warmly at her. 'Guess

I'm happy for you and Carl, Margret, after all,' he said.

'Thank you,' she said faintly. 'But please ... don't say anything to Laura yet. Or to Aunt Marion. You see, Carl wants to be here when we make the announcement. Please don't say anything to anyone until after he's come back on Friday.'

'Then you're not sure,' he accused, the warm happy expression fading from his face and being replaced by doubt.

'Yes, yes, I am,' she said hastily. 'It's just that I promised Carl not to tell anyone until he comes back. I've only told you because ... well, because you asked me to marry you too. Greg, don't you think you'd better do something about that cheque?'

'Eh?' He looked puzzled, completely thrown off balance by the sudden change of subject. 'What cheque?'

'The cheque you gave me. I think I dropped it in the street when we stopped in Salem on the way down. I can't find it anywhere and I'm afraid someone might try to cash it. So you'd best call your bank and stop it and then perhaps you'd write out another one for me and take me to a branch of your bank here to cash that. I haven't any money at all and I would like to have some to spend on clothes and things ... for when I get married.'

'Okay, okay, where's the phone?' He was still frowning doubtfully.

'In the writing room,' she said, springing to her

feet, knowing that if she hesitated at all he would go back to the matter of her marriage to Carl. 'This way.'

The cheque was stopped. Greg wrote out another and then drove Margret to a branch of his bank in the city to cash it. Safe in the knowledge that she coud now pay for a ticket if she was able to make a reservation on the next plane flying to London from Logan airport, Margret persuaded Greg to drive her to a shopping mall and leave her there. He was reluctant to leave her, but eventually his desire to go to the Athenaeum Library got the better of him and he went off after saying he would be calling in to see her the next day.

As soon as he had driven away Margret found a travel agency and asked if they could find out if there was a seat available on the next flight to London. She would have liked to have flown out that night, but all seats were booked, so she made a reservation on a British Airways flight leaving the next evening, Thursday. By the time Carl returned from Philadelphia on Friday she would be gone, would actually be in England. Pain twisted through her sharply and surprisingly. Miles and miles of ocean would separate them and she would never see him again. Never. Her mouth tightening, she braced herself against the pain. She wasn't going to think ahead any more. Like Carl, she wasn't going in for regrets.

But it was to her great relief that Aunt Marion

invited her to go to a symphony concert that night. Listening to good music always made her forget her problems and when she returned to the house, she went up to bed humming the theme from the slow movement of that most romantic of piano concertos, Beethoven's Fourth.

Once in bed, however, she began to wonder what had possessed her to say she and Carl were getting married before they flew out to Peru. Even reminding herself that her intentions had been of the best didn't ease her conscience. She had told Greg a deliberate lie and so morrow evening she was going to run away from that lie, leaving Carl to do the explaining.

Then she found herself wishing that it wasn't a lie. She wished it were true and that she and Carl were going to be married. Why? Oh, no! She groaned and twisted over on to her side, burying her face in the pillow. It couldn't have happened. She couldn't have fallen in love with Carl. She mustn't have fallen in love with him. She didn't want to be in love with him or any other man. Lying awake in the darkness, she examined her feelings and finally admitted to herself that it was possible, she was in love with Carl and that the lie she had told Greg had been the result of wishful thinking, no more, no less.

Not at all comforted by this conclusion, she fell into a troubled sleep from which she wakened suddenly with her nerves twanging, sure that she had heard the bedroom door open and someone enter the room. Sitting up, she listened and heard the slight sound of someone breathing.

'Who is it?' she demanded, her voice sounding unnaturally loud in the darkness.

'Me.'

At the same moment the bedside lamp clicked on and she saw Carl standing by the bed, hands in the pockets of a dark red velour dressing gown, belted at the waist, its lapels falling back from his bare chest.

'But . . . but . . . I thought you were in Philadelphia,' she whispered, rubbing a hand across her eyes, expecting him to have disappeared and the lamp to be off when she looked again, believing that she had thought about him so much before she had fallen asleep that she was experiencing one of those curious psychic phenomena and had *willed* him to be there in the room with her.

'I was there, but I flew back this evening. I've not been long in the house.' He noticed her rubbing at her eyes again and laughed softly. 'I'm here, really here,' he said. 'Feel.'

He sat down on the side of the bed and taking hold of one of her hands pressed it against his chest. Beneath her fingers and palm, hairs and skin felt slightly damp as if he had been in the shower and under them his heart beat strongly and regularly. That throbbing sensation under her fingertips affected her deeply. For a moment she felt she had touched the essence of the man.

'Convinced?' he asked, leaning towards her. In the lamplight his skin had the sheen of bronze and his eyes were dark and unrevealing. An unruly coil of sun-bleached hair slid forward over his forehead and he smelt of the soap he had used. Margret's senses reeled a little under the onslaught of his powerful maleness and she experienced a strong urge to fling her arms about him and make him welcome, she was so glad to see him. Afraid of the impulse, she withdrew, pulling her hand free of his grasp and pushing it under the bedclothes draped across her knees.

'I'm convinced,' she replied lightly. 'But what are you doing in my room?'

'Checking that you're still here. I had a feeling you might have left for England.'

It must be extra-sensory perception that had brought him to her room, she thought wildly. He had sensed she had been thinking about him. She had reached him on a level of communication which was beyond her control. Alarmed by the possibility, she leaned back against the headboard, as far away from him as possible, and stared at him with wide eyes.

'What's the matter?' he asked.

'Aunt Marion said you wouldn't be back until Friday,' she whispered. 'And I thought ... I believed you wouldn't come back at all, that you'd gone away for good to Peru.'

In the soft intimate glow of the lamplight they

stared at each other, glances shifting slightly to linger lovingly on the curve of a cheek, the shape of lips but always returning to the eyes. Margret felt her pulses race as if she were on the edge of making a new and wonderful discovery. Then Carl moved, stood up and strolled away into the shadows. The moments of closeness were over and she felt disappointment chill her.

'I had gone away for good,' he said, his voice floating back to her from somewhere near the window. 'I wasn't coming back here before flying to Peru. I guessed you'd go to England as soon as you knew I'd be away for a few days. Then I found that damned cheque in my wallet and realised you couldn't go anywhere without the money.'

'You mean the cheque Greg gave me?' she gasped.

'That's right. You dropped it in the motel foyer in Salem and I picked it up before going after you. I meant to give it to you when we arrived here, but I forgot.' He appeared out of the shadows again and taking a hand out of one of the pockets of his robe he placed an oblong piece of pink paper on the bedside table. 'There it is,' he said. 'A bit creased, but still good.'

Margret stared at the cheque and struggled to suppress a hysterical desire to burst out laughing.

'You came back just to give me that?' she whispered. 'You brought it back for me to tear it up?'

'Tear it up?' he snapped, his lips thinning, his

brows frowning. 'What the hell are you getting at?'

'Greg came here this afternoon,' she said as if that explained everything.

'He came here? Why?'

'He said he'd come to study in a library of some sort. But that was only an excuse. He really came to stop me from going away with you.'

'And how did he intend to do that?' Carl's voice was amused.

'He asked me to marry him.'

There was a heavy silence. She looked up at him. In the loom of lamplight his face was mask-like, hard and fixed, betraying nothing of what he was thinking or feeling.

'Is that what you hoped he would do?' he said at last. 'Is that why you came away with me? Did you hope to rouse him into taking some action?'

'No . . . I mean yes. I did want him to take some action, but not that,' she said rather wildly. 'Oh, I thought you knew why I left Lindley's Point with you.'

'I thought I did, too,' he said dryly, his mouth twisting cynically. 'Are you going to marry him?'

'No, of course I'm not. I told him to go back to Maine and ask Laura to marry him. But he said she wouldn't agree to marry him while you're still un-married because she's still in love with you, so I told him. . . .' She broke off, hesitating to confess, unsure of how he would react.

'What did you tell him?' Carl prompted curiously.

'I ... I told him that you and I are going to be married here in Boston before we go to Peru,' she whispered, her head bowed.

There was another silence, so heavy that it weighed down on her, crushing her into the bed. She had a great desire to fling the bedclothes over her head to hide from him, she was so embarrassed by what she had done and so sure he would be angry. After a while she dared to glance at him, but he wasn't there.

'Carl?' she said uncertainly, wondering if she had imagined he had been in the room after all. But the lamp was still on and she knew she hadn't switched it on.

'Yeah?' His voice came from the direction of the windows again.

'I'm sorry I told him that. It was all I could think of at the time to convince Greg that he's wrong about Laura and you, and I didn't think it would matter since you wouldn't be coming back here and I would be going to England.'

Did it convince him?'

'Not completely.'

'So there's more?'

'Yes, there's more,' she sighed. 'He said he won't believe we're going to be married until he sees it happen. He says he's going to stay right here in Boston and be your best man. He's going to ask Laura to drive the children down here so that she can be present at the ceremony and maybe she'll be convinced at last that you're not going to ask her to go with you to Peru.'

More silence, lasting so long that her nerves were stretched to breaking point, when Carl spoke again, and she jumped at the sound of his voice.

'Does anyone else know that we're going to be married besides Greg?' His voice was cool and calm.

'I asked him not to say anything to Laura or to Aunt Marion because you wanted to be here when it was announced.' She paused, then added, 'You're angry with me, aren't you?'

'Why should I be?'

'Because I've put you in a difficult position. I'm sorry. I shouldn't have lied to Greg. Now we'll have to tell him we're not getting married.'

'We'll only have to do that if we don't get married,' he said, coming across to stand at the end of the bed.

'What do you mean?' she whispered, her heart beginning to pound.

'There's no reason why we shouldn't see it through if it's one sure way of convincing Greg and Laura neither of us wants to marry either of them.' His mouth twisted into its taunting grin. 'I realise it's a bit late in the day for me to propose to you since you've already gone ahead and told a member of my family that we're going to be married, but I'll do it anyway, Margret, if I marry you first, here in Boston, will you fly with me to Peru?'

He was too much in the shadows for her to see

the expression on his face, but she had the impression that he was very amused by the situation in which she had placed both of them by her lie to Greg, and she felt anger surge through her because he could make fun of something as serious as a proposal of marriage.

'*O spite! O hell! I see you are all bent*
To set against me for your merriment,'

she muttered, clasping her head between her hands and feeling tears spurt suddenly in her eyes.

'What the hell are you talking about now?' he demanded irritably.

'It's a quotation from *A Midsummer Night's Dream*, the play by Shakespeare I went to see with Brett. Helena says those words when she's pursued by Lysander and Demetrius. She can't believe that either of them are serious when they both seem to want to marry her. You're proposing to me to mock me because I told Greg we're going to be married. I didn't mean what I said to Greg and I wouldn't have said it if I'd known you would be coming back here.'

'But it was a good idea and I think we should go through with it and get married,' Carl said calmly.

'You're not the marrying kind,' she cried. 'You told me so yourself, and Greg knows it too. That's why he's doubtful.'

'All the more reason why we should go through with it,' he said as he came round the bed to sit close to her. 'I'll ask you again. Will you marry me, Margret?'

'You're not serious,' she objected.

'Sure I am. There's time for us to marry before going to Peru. It takes only three days to get a licence in this State and once we have the licence we can marry any time we like.'

'But . . . but I've booked a reservation on a flight to England tomorrow night,' she argued weakly.

'That isn't a very good reason for refusing to marry me,' he taunted dryly. 'You'll have to do better than that. You can always cancel the reservation.'

'We can't get married. We can't!' she whispered, her head bowed, her hair falling forward across her cheeks.

'Why can't we?'

She was silent as she tried to find a reason for not marrying him, one that he would believe, and found none.

'You want to help Greg, don't you?' he said quietly. 'You want him to do the right thing for his own happiness?'

'Yes, I do,' she said, looking up quickly. He was watching her with narrowed eyes.

'Then you'll marry me. I owe it to Laura to undo the harm I did to her and him by taking Liza to Lindley's Point ten years ago. If anyone is to blame for their unhappiness, it's me,' he said with a touch of bitterness. 'And if my marriage is the only way of getting them together then I'm quite prepared to marry you.'

'But afterwards,' she whispered. 'What will we do after we're married?'

'We'll live together like other married couples do,' he replied with a glint of humour.

'But supposing it doesn't work?'

'Then we'll split, I guess,' he said slowly, frowning.

'For me marriage is a very serious step to take,' she muttered, wondering how she could make him understand why she was suspicious of his proposal.

'You think it's any different for me?' he retorted.

Yes, I do. You're not asking me to marry you because you love me,' she challenged him defiantly.

'What do you know about love?' he jeered, moving closer to her, dominating her again by his physical magnetism, his tanned skin furred with golden hairs, his eyes burning darkly as they looked into hers.

'I know it's more than you feel for me,' she countered.

'And what do I feel for you?' he queried softly, raising a hand to touch her cheek, his fingers as light as thistledown as they slid over her skin.

'It's just physical, nothing more,' she replied, holding herself stiffly, trying to ignore the tremors of sensuousness that were shaking through her.

'I admit it,' he murmured, touching her hair, stroking a swathe of it back behind her ear, his glance narrowing on her mouth. 'I'm attracted by your midnight-dark hair and your golden eyes.' He leaned forward and touched each of her eyes with his lips. 'By that mysterious little smile which tilts your lips when you're thinking up ways to elude me. I'm attracted by your fine white skin and beautiful long legs. I've wanted you ever since I laid eyes on you. That's why I asked you to fly to Peru with me.'

'Wanting should never be confused with loving,' she retorted primly, the delicate pink colour that washed over her face betraying the fact that she was shaken by what he had said.

'I can't agree,' he argued. 'It can be the beginning of loving.' He moved even closer so that she was completely trapped. 'And you're not going to deny that what you feel for me is exactly what I feel for you. You're not going to deny that you like to touch me as much as I like touching you, because I know differently.'

Warm and sensual, his lips touched hers, parting them gently. For a second Margret resisted, but she couldn't fight for long the desire that was rumbling inside her like a raging volcano. It erupted suddenly, melting her stiffness, and with a sighing groan of pleasure she put her arms around him.

For a while they sought and discovered each other's hidden delights. With lips and hands they spoke to each other. Without words they created a poem of joyous sensuousness, of bodily worship and praise that stopped only when Carl's voice, soft and slightly breathless, interrupted it.

'Tomorrow we'll tell Aunt Marion at breakfast that we're going to be married. Once she knows you can be sure she'll call Greg's parents and tell them.

That way he'll find out that we're going through with the wedding,' he whispered. He put his lips to her ear. 'You haven't said yes yet, honey.'

'I thought I had, just now,' she replied shyly.

'But I like to hear it as well as feel it,' he murmured.

Dare she trust him? Was marriage really for them? The choice was hers. She could draw back from the edge of commitment now and say no. Or she could take the plunge. Nothing in her background or upbringing had prepared her for this moment. She had no guidelines to direct her and no prompter sat in the wings, reminding her of the next words. She had only a strong gut feeling to be with Carl as often as possible, to see him every day, if she could. And yet she was still unsure of him.

'Yes,' she whispered impulsively before she could change her mind again.

'Thank you,' He kissed her and slid off the bed.

'Where are you going now?' she asked.

'Back to my own room to bed,' he replied, drawing his robe about him and tightening the belt. He stifled a yawn with the back of his hand. 'I'm bushed after leaving here early yesterday morning, spending the day in conference with my bosses in Philadelphia and then flying back. And I hadn't reckoned on being kept until after two this morning by you.'

'Well, you didn't have to come in here,' she retorted breathlessly, pushing up on her elbow and glaring in his direction, irritated with herself because she was disappointed because he wasn't going to stay the rest of the night with her.

'But aren't you glad I did come to see you?' he challenged tauntingly from the doorway. 'I'd have liked to have stayed longer,' he added softly in answer to her thought, 'but I guess that can wait now until we've both taken vows before witnesses. See you at breakfast. Sleep well!'

The door closed behind him. All was quiet in the shadowy lamplit room. Only the light slanting out from under the parchment-coloured shade was proof that Carl had been in the room, Margret thought, as she switched it off and lay down again. Only the light and the tumultuous state of her mind and body. Sleep well, he had said. Turning, she punched at her pillow with a fist, frustration screaming through her and tying knots in her stomach. Sleep well! How was she going to sleep now?

She flung herself on to her back again and stared at the loom of street lights through the window. Had Carl really been in this room tonight and had he really asked her to marry him? Had she really said she would marry him? Marriage. The word seemed to dance in flaming letters before her. Marriage without love. Oh, what had she done? What had she done?

Surprisingly she fell asleep immediately, but when she awoke she didn't feel at all rested and still had an uneasy feeling that she might have imagined all that had happened in the bedroom during the night. Only when she went into the small breakfast room next to the kitchen and saw Carl, big and tawny, in jeans and a short-sleeved dark blue leisure shirt, sitting opposite to Aunt Marion did some of the uneasy feeling evaporate.

'Margret, I'm so happy for you!' Marion was on her feet and coming towards her with outstretched arms, her thin lined face smiling, her blue-grey eyes twinkling. She kissed Margret on the cheek and hugged her. 'Carl has just told me. It's something I've always hoped for. Earl, my husband, would have been delighted, I know. My only regret is that it has to be done in such a hurry. Still, I mustn't complain too much. At least it's going to be done here in this house.' She looked back at Carl. 'I'm going now to call Phyllis and tell her.' She turned to Margret again. 'She's Greg's mother. I guess she'll want to come over right away to meet you.'

Marion went from the room and Margret took a seat at the table. Picking up the coffee pot, Carl filled a cup for her.

'As soon as we're through we'll go and get the licence,' he said crisply. 'I don't think we'll have any trouble getting one. Do you have a medical certificate?'

'No. Is it necessary that I have one?'

'Yes. To prove that you're sound in mind and body.' He frowned. 'Perhaps Aunt Marion can arrange for you to see her doctor this morning.'

'Supposing I refuse to see a doctor?' she challenged.

Across the table his eyes, acid blue in the morning light, studied her.

'Changed your mind?' he asked softly. 'If you have, Aunt Marion is going to be most distressed. She thinks you're the nicest woman I've ever brought home and she's glad I'm going to marry you.'

'Carl, do we have to go through with the actual ceremony here? Couldn't we say there isn't time to do it before going to Peru, but we'll be married when we get there?' she whispered.

'Got cold feet this morning, haven't you, sweetheart?' he jeered, his mouth twisting unpleasantly. 'Have you forgotten Greg? He won't believe I'm married until he sees it happen, so you told me. We have to get married here, if we're going to do it at all.'

'But——' she began, and broke off as Marion returned to the room.

'Phyllis and Greg will be over right away,' Marion said smugly. 'They were astounded, as I guessed they would be. Now, is there anything else I should do this morning to be helping things along?'

'You could take Margret to see Dr Seifert,' said Carl smoothly. 'She needs a medical certificate before we can get a licence.'

'Of course,' beamed Marion. 'I'll call his secretary right now and make the appointment. What about your people, Margret, in England? Have you told them? Will any of them want to fly over for the ceremony?'

'I . . . er . . . I don't have any family . . . that is, no one near, only my stepmother . . . and she won't want to come. She wouldn't be able to afford to fly over at such short notice. No . . . no, there's no one.'

'Then we'll be your family,' said Marion kindly, touching her briefly on the shoulder. 'Oh, it's so exciting!' she burbled as she went towards the door again. 'I've always wanted to have a wedding to plan.'

'You see?' Carl hissed across the table. 'Back out now and you'll have one extremely unhappy Marion Lindley.'

'Blackmailer!' Margret retorted, and watched him grin. 'Don't you have any second thoughts?'

'Not about this.' He leaned towards her, his eyes darkening as they looked into hers. 'You see, I'll be getting something I want. You.'

Suddenly the magic of the previous night was swirling around her, putting to flight her doubts. All her arguments against being married faded from her mind and her hand reached out across the table towards him. His hand came up to cover it. Nothing more was said between them, because Marion re-entered the room and announced that Dr Seifert would see Margret at his office in exactly half an hour and she would accompany her to his office.

From that moment on, through the next five

sunny hot days a sense of unreality, of being caught in a magic spell which she could not break, increased for Margret as she was swept along by Marion through the excited planning of the wedding. The feeling persisted right up to the hour of two o'clock on a sticky, humid afternoon, when, wearing a short white dress with orange blossom scattered among her silky dark hair, she stood beside Carl in the sitting room of the old house where a Lindley had lived for over a hundred years and promised to be his wife.

CHAPTER SIX

THE wedding ceremony was over. They had ex-
changed vows and rings. Outside as if to accent the
drama of the occasion nature played up with violent
stage effects. In a charcoal grey and sulphur yellow
sky lightning flashed with a livid green light. Thunder growled ceaselessly and rain fell as if poured
from hundreds of buckets in steady streams of water,
blotting out the view of the houses on the opposite
side of the street.

Inside the elegant sitting room lights blazed from
glass chandeliers, champagne sparkled in fine crystal
goblets. Eyes glittered, teeth flashed against sun-
tanned skin and voices rumbled and shrilled in conversation and laughter as the guests mingled. Shaking hands with people she had never met before,
smiling and smiling, Margret played her part,
acting out the scene. Soon the curtain would come
down and she would become herself again, Margret
Randall, single woman, free to go where she liked,
independent, beholden to no man.

'I hope you'll be very happy, Margret.' Greg was
beside her, his hand, warm and slightly moist with
sweat, clasped hers and his lips were soft as he
saluted the bride in the traditional way.

But his dark eyes held a strained expression and

the familiar anxious frown creased his forehead.

'I feel responsible for all this,' he sighed, taking her arm and guiding her over to the window embrasure where they could talk without being overheard.

'Why?' she asked. Surely he hadn't guessed at the truth, that this marriage would not have taken place if it hadn't been necessary to convince him?'

'It goes back a long way,' he said. 'To the day you came to my house in England to be interviewed. If you hadn't agreed to work for me and if you hadn't agreed to come over here with me and hadn't gone to Lindley's Point you wouldn't have met Carl. So I feel responsible.'

'You shouldn't feel like that,' she told him, looking past him. On the other side of the room she could see Laura talking to Carl. Their heads were close together and they were whispering like two conspirators. Even while she watched them Laura looked across right at her, then turned and said something else to Carl and they laughed. A strange feeling that they were laughing at her overwhelmed Margret suddenly and she had to suppress an urge to go over to them and demand why they were laughing at her.

'I can't help feeling you've been trapped into this marriage by . . . well, by all of us,' said Greg.

'Trapped?' she exclaimed, looking at him in alarm. Then she remembered she was playing a part; the part of the happy woman who had just married the man she loved. 'Oh, no!' She thought her laughter sounded genuine. 'I haven't been trapped into anything. I've married Carl because ... because I want to be married to him, and for no other reason.'

'I guess it's because it all happened so quickly that I feel that way,' he muttered apologetically.

'Remember we married here today because we wanted to please Aunt Marion,' she said quietly. 'She's wanted to arrange a wedding in the family for so long. Your mother, too.'

'Yeah, yeah, I guess so.' His glance avoided hers as he rumpled his hair with one hand, obviously not satisfied by her answer.

'Don't worry about it, Greg. Carl and I understand one another very well. We'll be all right, honestly.' She put a hand on his arm and smiled up at him. 'I'm glad you and Heather and Jamie were here,' she told him. 'Not having any family of my own here, I felt you and they were my family.'

'Nice of you to say that, Margret,' he replied, covering her hand with his and smiling back warmly. 'I hope you'll always feel that way about the kids and me, because for a while we were a family, weren't we? God knows we've missed you since you left Lindley's Point and I don't know how to replace you. My mother says Heather and Jamie can live with her, here in Boston, go to school where I went to school until I can find someone to take your place. . . .'

'But surely . . . I mean, I thought that now Carl is

married you'd go ahead and ask Laura to marry you,' exclaimed Margret, disconcerted by what he had said.

'I don't know whether I will,' he muttered. He flicked a glance in the direction of Laura, who was still talking to Carl. 'She's really upset by his marriage to you, much more upset than I thought she would be. It was difficult to persuade her to accept the invitation. She said she had the feeling that this marriage of yours is all a hoax. . . .'

'Now, now, Greg, don't monopolise the bride!' said a hearty male voice nearby. 'Congratulations, Margret. I'm Brad Mason, an old buddy of Carl's. We were in the Marines together.'

Her hand was engulfed by a huge red paw, her cheek was kissed and she was drawn away from Greg towards Aunt Marion, who was standing by the long table on which food was set out in buffet style.

'Time for you and Carl to cut the cake,' said Marion. 'Put your hand over Margret's, Carl, while she holds the knife. I'd like you in this, Greg, with Heather and Jamie. And Phyllis and Gordon. It's to be a family portrait for the local newspapers, just to show we Lindleys are still alive and kicking!'

The cake was cut. Photographers' lights flashed as pictures were taken. Carl bent towards Margret.

'As soon as this is over go upstairs and change, and I'll meet you in the kitchen. We'll slide out by the back door. I don't want a whole crowd of them coming with us to the airport to see us off. The plane for Miami, where we'll spend the night, takes off in an hour and we should be there thirty minutes before to check in and get our seats.'

It took Margret several minutes to escape from the room, so many people delayed her on her way, but at last she was able to run upstairs to her room. Once the door was closed she sagged with relief. This was the interlude between the acts. For a short while she could be alone and gather her strength for the next scene.

Going over to the bed, she sank down on it and stared at the wide gold band Carl had placed on her finger. Was it all a hoax, as Laura had suggested to Greg? She twisted the ring on her finger, thinking of the vows she and Carl had taken. They had been real enough. The licence was real and Judge Lindley, before whom they had made their promises, was certainly authorised by law to perform the marriage ceremony.

So that part wasn't a hoax. That had really happened. Someone knocked at the door, and thinking Marion had come to hurry her along, Margret called to her to enter. The door opened and Laura stepped into the room.

'I saw you escaping,' she said, her bright smile flashing across her face, 'and I guessed why. I thought you might like some help.' She closed the door and approached the bed. 'You're looking pale. Are you okay?'

'Yes, thank you. I have a slight headache, that's all.' Margret managed a smile. 'Thunder always gives me a headache.'

'The storm seems to be over now.' Laura looked round the room. 'What are you going to wear to go away in?'

'There's a green ultra-suede suit hanging in the closet,' Margret replied, standing up. She unpinned the corsage of red and white roses from the front of her dress. 'Could you undo the zip for me, please?' she asked, turning her back to Laura.

The wedding dress was taken off and Laura laid it on the bed, straightening out the folds of the skirt with careful hands.

'Are you taking the dress with you?' she said.

'No. Aunt Marion says I can leave it here for the time being,' answered Margret. 'I've packed everything else and my cases are already in the car.' She slipped into the thin sheer nylon blouse she intended to wear with the suit.

When she was dressed she sat down in front of the dressing table to attend to her make-up and hair, hoping Laura would leave her by herself for a few minutes. She needed more time to be Margret Randall and prepare herself for the next scene in which she would be Margret Lindley. But Laura didn't go. She lingered by the window.

'Thanks for your help,' Margret said firmly.

'You're welcome,' Laura replied, and went to stand behind Margret. Reflected in the mirror she was a tall, full-breasted woman with a square

tanned face, not beautiful or pretty, but strong-look-
ing, dependable. She was wearing a silky, figure-
moulding dress in navy blue and white and her cool
grey eyes were shaded by a wide-brimmed white hat.
'I wish there'd been time for you and me to know
each other better,' she said.

'I wish there had been, too,' replied Margret pol-
itely.

'I'm very fond of Carl,' Laura went on. 'And at
one time I was in love with him.' She looked
directly at Margret's reflected wary golden eyes.
'Then ten years ago I realised I wasn't in love with
him any more. I realised I preferred Greg.' Her
generously moulded lips curved into a bitter smile.
'Realisation only came when he eloped with Liza,'
she added dryly.

'You don't have to tell me any more,' Margret
said quickly, rising to her feet and picking up the
tan-coloured envelope handbag which matched the
tan-coloured high-heeled sandals she was wearing. 'I
must go. Carl is waiting.'

'No, wait.' Laura stepped in front of her. 'I have
to tell you that when I heard there was a young
woman . . . a very pretty young woman . . . staying
at Lindley's Point this summer with Greg and his
children, I was so jealous I could have scratched
your eyes out. Rumour in Roskeag had it that you
were Greg's mistress and would probably marry him
one day.' Laura's mouth twisted again and she
noticed Margret's start of surprise. 'Didn't you know
everyone was talking about you? I believed the

stories that were going about and I couldn't get it out of my head that you were another Liza, come between Greg and me.'

'You were at your house in Maine those first two weeks I was there?' exclaimed Margret. 'Then why didn't you come over to see me and find out the truth for yourself?'

'I was afraid, I think, that I might find out that the stories were true,' said Laura. 'I knew that Carl was here; in Boston, on leave from his job in Peru, so I called him and told him about you. He said he'd come up and check the stories out for me.'

'Oh. So he knew I was staying at Lindley's Point all the time. He knew I was in the house and yet he. . . .' Margret broke off, frowning as she tried to remember all that Carl had said to her the night he had arrived at Lindley's Point.

'Yes, he knew,' said Laura. 'And he agreed to take you away for a few days so that Greg and I could meet again without you being there. Then he persuaded you to leave and come to Boston with him. That would have been great, only Greg decided to follow you here. He was worried in case Carl had taken advantage of you.' Laura laughed a little and shook her head. 'Greg's always been very chivalrous, always rushing to the rescue of fair damsels he believes to be in distress.' She paused and gave Margret one of her icy stares. 'I know he asked you to marry him,' she added.

'Yes, he did. That's why. . . .' Margret's voice faded into silence and she bit her lip.

'That's why you and Carl announced your forth-coming marriage,' Laura said, and sighed heavily. 'I guessed that was what had happened. I guessed that today's little performance was just that, a show put on for the rest of us.'

'But we were legally married,' argued Margret.

'I've no doubt about that, but I didn't think Carl would go this far,' said Laura, turning away to pace up and down the room. 'I didn't realise he cared so much about me to do what he has done—I guess what I'm trying to say is that I know he doesn't love you and that you don't love him and that you're not going to stay married.'

Margret glanced at her watch and hurried to-wards the door. She didn't like what Laura was saying and didn't want to hear any more.

'I must go,' she muttered. 'Please don't say any-thing more about your suspicions to Greg,' she added as she opened the door, 'I hope everything works out for the best between you and him.'

'But you don't seem to realise, you and Carl didn't have to go as far as actually getting married,' Laura said urgently.

'Goodbye,' said Margret firmly, and closed the bedroom door after her.

She managed to reach the kitchen without being seen by any of the guests. Carl was there, looking impatient. He hurried her through the back door and down some steps to an alleyway where Marion's chauffeur-driven car was waiting.

'Thank God that's over,' he said as he settled in a

corner of the back seat. 'I'm not going to get married again, ever. I hate that sort of fuss.'

Margret glanced at him. In a grey pin-striped suit and pale blue shirt he looked very different from the casually clothed man she had sailed with, but even as she looked at him he was loosening the knot of his tie and undoing the top button of his shirt, obviously disliking the restraint of formal clothes.

The car turned on to the road which led to the airport which was only a few miles from the centre of the city. The dark clouds which had brought the thunderstorm were rolling away towards the east and sunlight was glittering on the concrete and glass of the high-rise buildings which towered behind the sloping roofs, gables and mellow brick walls of the old part of the city. Out on the wide bay wind ruffled the water, which was fast changing from storm grey to sunny white-crested blue, and on the scattered islands sandy beaches glinted pale yellow.

'Carl, I'm not coming with you to Peru.' Margret spoke steadily, keeping her eyes on the grey airport terminal buildings which were looming ahead. She betrayed nothing of the confusion and bewilderment which were raging within her as a result of her conversation with Laura. It was time, she had decided, to stop pretending.

'Why not?' His voice was quiet.

'It isn't necessary for me to go with you, not now that Greg has seen us get married.'

'I was under the impression that you regard marriage as a serious step,' he said dryly.

'I do. And that's why I can't go with you to Peru.' She turned to him and flinched back when she saw how acid blue his eyes were, how hard his face. 'Oh, why continue to pretend?' she whispered, aware that Alfred the chauffeur might be listening. 'We went through with the wedding ceremony only to convince Greg and he won't know we haven't gone away together. No one will know for a long time that we've split, and by then Greg and Laura will be married,' she explained.

Carl didn't reply immediately and the car drew up in front of the entrance to one of the terminal buildings. Alfred got out and went round to the trunk of the car to take out their cases.

'You'll have to pretend a little longer,' Carl said abruptly, his voice savagely quiet and controlled, his eyes colder than ever, deep lines graven into his lean cheeks as he set his teeth. 'If Alfred doesn't see us apparently going away together he'll tell Aunt Marion and then everyone will know it was a pretence ... too soon. You'll come with me into the building and at least as far as the airline's desk.'

'Oh, all right,' she muttered.

Alfred went with them, helping to carry the cases. No one was at the desk and by the time Margret had caught up with Carl he had already handed over the tickets to the clerk. Before she could stop him Alfred lifted her cases on to the scales, said goodbye to both her and Carl and walked away. Margret reached forward to take her cases off the scales just as the ticket clerk slipped a label on one of them and pulled it off to place it on a conveyor belt.

'My case!' she exclaimed turning to Carl. 'It's gone!'

'We'd like seats in the non-smoking area,' said Carl to the clerk, ignoring her.

'But I'm not going with you,' she hissed, going close to him.

He glanced sideways at her. There was a grim determined slant to his mouth and his eyes were as hard as blue glass.

'I'll check you in just the same,' he replied tautly. 'It's possible that between now and take-off time you'll have changed your mind. *Again!*'

'No. Never!' she retorted fiercely, and then realising that the ticket clerk was staring at her with raised eyebrows and the few people who were standing in line behind Carl were also curious, she turned away and marched towards the rest-rooms.

In the women's room she shut herself into one of the lavatories, determined to stay in there until the plane had taken off for Miami. It was the only way she could think of to convince Carl that she meant what she said.

Several times she heard the Miami flight called and several times she heard her own name called. She was asked to report to the airline desk. Once a woman came into the rest-room and banged on each of the lavatory doors asking if there was a Mrs Margret Lindley there. Suspecting that the woman was an airline employee sent in by Carl, Margret didn't answer. Soon the plane would take off. Carl would be gone, on his way to Peru, and she would be free to return to England. Their brief marriage would be over.

She waited for about fifteen minutes after the take-off time before she left the toilet and then she lingered another ten minutes, combing her hair, washing her hands and planning what to do next. In her handbag she found the folder containing the ticket to London which she had bought. It was still valid. All she needed was a new seat reservation, so she would go to the British Airways terminal building and find out if there was a seat vacant on the flight which was due to leave for England that evening.

Cautiously she pushed open the door of the rest-room and stepped out. There were many more people in the departure area, lining up to check luggage for the next flights out. Margret began to walk towards the exit, looking about her all the time, looking for Carl but not expecting to see him. Near the exit she collided with someone and looked up into hard blue eyes ablaze with a wicked anger.

'What the hell are you playing at?' he drawled, his voice purring threateningly. 'We've missed the flight to Miami.'

'I know. I intended to miss it. I'm not going with you.' She licked suddenly dry lips, more jolted than she was prepared to admit to find him still there.

'Why didn't you go?' she asked.

'I was waiting for you to come out of the rest-room,' he said tautly. He was very pale. 'Haven't you forgotten something? Haven't you forgotten we were married this afternoon? We made promises to each other,' he went on softly. 'And I think that gives me the right to ask you why—all of a sudden—you're wanting to split before we've tried being married to each other.'

'I've told you. I know you married me only to convince Greg and help Laura, so I thought I'd make it easy for you to end the marriage by not coming with you. We'll split now instead of later. I still have the ticket I bought to go to London, so I thought I'd go over to British Airways now and see if I can make a reservation on this evening's flight.'

His hands slid from her shoulders. His eyes narrow, he stared down at her, frowning slightly. Then he shrugged his shoulders.

'Okay. I'll come with you,' he drawled equably, and took hold of her arm just above the elbow as they walked towards the exit doors. 'It's a good way from here and we'll have to go on the airport bus.'

Outside there was a line of people waiting for the inter-terminal bus. There were also a few taxis parked by the kerb of the sidewalk. Carl raised his free hand and one of the cabs slid to a stop beside them. He opened the back door and urged Margret towards the interior of the car.

'I'd prefer to go on the bus,' she said, suddenly

suspicious, half turning to him and at the same time trying to free her arm from his grasp.

'This will be quicker,' he replied coolly.

He gave her a push, and she lost her balance and fell awkwardly on to the back seat of the car. By the time she had recovered and her hand was reaching for the lever of the other door to open it Carl was in the car too and it was moving forward. His arm came about her shoulders and he hauled her back against him.

'You'll only hurt yourself if you try to get out now,' he whispered into her hair.

Resisting a desire to relax against him, she pushed free and leaned towards the taxi-driver.

'Please take us to the British Airways terminal.' she said coolly.

'You want me to do what she says, sir?' drawled the driver, his dark face impassive as he drove round to the main exit road.

'No. Drive to the Pilgrims' Inn. Know where it is?' said Carl, also leaning forward as he took his wallet from his pocket.

'Along the coast somewhere, towards Cape Cod. Going to cost you some,' said the driver toughly.

Carl took a crisp twenty-dollar bill from his wallet and handed it to the man.

'You'll get the rest when we arrive at the Inn,' he said.

'Okay, sir. You're the boss.' The driver gave Margret an apologetic grin over his shoulder. 'Sorry, ma'am, but money talks in this town.'

'So it seems,' she retorted, and flung herself back in the corner of the seat, refusing to look at Carl. 'Where are we going?' she demanded.

'Somewhere where we can be alone, on this the first night of our marriage, where we can dine by candlelight, at an inn I know of along the coast. It caters for honeymooners.' Mockery edged his voice as he leaned back beside her.

'I'm not going to spend the night with you,' she flared.

'You're not going to spend it with anyone else,' he retorted grimly. 'No one cheats on me and gets away with it, not even you.'

'I . . . I haven't cheated you!' she exclaimed furiously, turning on him.

'But you were intending to cheat,' he drawled. 'Last week you said you would go with me to Peru if I married you first. Now we're married and you're refusing to go with me. I call that intent to cheat.' He paused, heaved a sigh and raked a hand through his hair. 'I should have known better,' he added with a touch of weariness. 'But I thought that at last, in you, I'd met a woman I could trust.'

He moved away then, sliding over to the other corner, turning away from her to look out at the traffic through which they were dodging as they left the city behind. Disconcerted and more than hurt by his view of her behaviour, Margret sat for a while in miserable silence also looking out until she remembered her luggage.

'Where are my cases?' she asked.

'On their way to Miami, with mine,' he replied dryly. 'Don't worry about them. They'll wait there for us—I arranged that with the airline when I realised neither of us would be going on that flight.'

'You should have gone,' she muttered tonelessly.

'Not without you.'

'But what about your job?'

'It can wait until I've sorted out my personal affairs, and right now you're my personal affair . . . very personal.' His voice grated oddly. 'And I'm beginning to wish I'd never gone to Lindley's Point, wish to God I'd never met you.' Violence throbbed in his voice now.

'And I wish I hadn't met you!' she cried in a low voice, hurt beyond bearing, and looked out of the window again, seeing everything through a blur of tears.

No more was said. Music from the taxi's radio blared noisily, a singer of country music sang about the woman he had left behind in some town, but Margret didn't hear the words because other words were repeating themselves over and over in her mind; words from a poem by Burns, her memory of them triggered off by Carl's violent repudiation of their meeting ·

Had we never lov'd sae kindly,
Had we never lov'd sae blindly,
Never, met—or never parted,
We had ne'er been broken-hearted.

If she and Carl had never met, never gone cruising together, they wouldn't be here now, bound to each other in marriage and wishing they had never met.

All signs of the thunderstorm had gone from the sky by the time the car turned off the road down a lane that twisted towards the sea. Soon the ocean came into view. Dazzled with golden light from the westering sun, it stretched away to a hazy purple horizon. Far out some yachts were sailing, the white triangles of their sails glimmering.

The taxi stopped in the driveway of a pleasant rambling old colonial-styled house. Carl paid the driver another forty dollars and the man was suitably grateful. Up a shallow flight of steps to the pillared portico Margret went, conscious of Carl's hand at her elbow, knowing there was no possibility of her running out on him again.

The entrance hall of the house was luxuriously furnished and the reception clerk smiling and discreet, diplomatically disguising any surprise he might be feeling when Carl told him they had no luggage. They were shown to a room on the second floor by a bellboy. It was furnished with two double beds and simple pinewood chest of drawers. The window had a view of the ocean.

'It's a lovely room,' said Margret. She had decided on the drive out to be cool and calm. 'When can we eat?'

'Later.' Carl took off his jacket and hung it up in the closet. He removed his tie and flicked undone some of the buttons of his shirt as if he were too hot, yet he went to the window and closed it, cutting off the sound of surf falling on some unseen beach. 'Let me take your jacket,' he said, coming up behind her and putting his hands on her shoulders, suggestion in his touch.

'No, thanks. I'll keep it on.' Shivering a little in spite of the warmth of the room, she moved away from him, only to find he had slipped her handbag from beneath her arm where it had been tucked. 'What are you doing?' she exclaimed, going back to him and reaching out for the bag. 'Give it to me!'

He took the ticket folder out and handed the bag back to her. Flicking open the folder, he removed the ticket and studied it.

'One-way, huh?' he murmured.

'Yes. That's all I could afford. Please give it back to me.'

'No.'

'Don't you dare!' she seethed, guessing he was going to destroy it and snatching at it. The flimsy paper tore across. 'Oh, no!' she wailed. 'Now look what you've done!'

'I'm always to blame, aren't I?' he retorted, as he tore the ticket again, several times so that all that remained were small pieces which he dropped in the waste backet.

'Why did you do that?' she demanded.

'So you can't get away in a hurry,' Carl replied.

'Oh, how you like to bulldoze people!' she flung

at him. 'How you like to push them where they don't want to go! You're an arrogant bully and you had no right to destroy my ticket.'

'And you're nothing but a two-timing cheat,' he snarled. 'You're always pretending to be what you're not. You're always putting on an act.' He stepped over to her. His hands curved about her waist. 'You thought you could get away with deceiving me like you deceived Greg, didn't you? But I'm not Greg and I'm not going to let you go without making you pay the full price of deceit. We're going to celebrate our marriage in the time-honoured way, here and now. Then you can leave— if you'll want to, that is.' His voice softened silkily as he slid the jacket from her shoulders and arms. He let it drop to the floor and taking hold of her shoulders pulled her towards him. 'Seems to me everyone got to kiss the bride at the reception except me,' he whispered.

'Carl, please!' Her hands were against his chest to keep him at bay. 'Wait!'

'Not any longer. You've challenged me and eluded me once too often, Margret. This is where it stops.'

His hand was rough under her chin, forcing her to look at him. She glimpsed his eyes glittering between thick lashes, the shine of his teeth behind his slightly parted lips, and felt desire leap up and spread through her. As his lips touched her mouth her lips were already parting to invite the invasion of his. Sighing, she swayed against him, expanding under the caresses of his hands like parched earth expands under the touch of rain.

Slowly her blouse was stroked away from her and joined her jacket on the floor. His fingers were warm and light against her skin while his mouth still took its toll of sweetness from hers. But her hands were busy too, sweeping aside his shirt, luxuriating in the muscled firmness of his body, in the roughness of hairs and the satin smoothness of skin.

Beyond the window light faded from the sky. In the room lamplight lapped them in a rosy glow as they lay on the bed breast to breast, thigh to thigh, kissing deeply and searchingly, lips moist and quivering, hands stroking and seeking, until at last passion burst forth and broke down the final barrier.

Hazily Margret became aware of a delicious lassitude in her limbs while other parts of her still throbbed and tingled. She hadn't known making love could be both pleasure and pain. She hadn't known she would want to weep at the same time that she wanted to shout with the sheer joy of being alive. Why did she feel this sudden all-pervading sadness? Was it because it had been done without love?

Suddenly she was sitting up, her hands over her face, crying silently, tears pouring from between her fingers to drop on her bare skin and on Carl. He surged up beside her, big, warm and golden. His arms went around her. With her face pressed against his chest she sobbed and sniffled.

'What's wrong?' he whispered, his fingers in her hair as he sought to comfort her. 'I tried to be gentle. It will be better next time, sweetheart. . . .'

'No, no, it won't,' she cried, trying to free herself and failing. 'Not without love,' she sobbed. 'I promised myself I would never do it without love.'

'You don't love me?' He sounded surprised and even laughed a little. 'That's funny, I got the impression just now that you do.'

'Oh, no!' She beat at his chest with her fists. 'That isn't what I mean. You always twist what I say. It's you. You don't love me. Oh, what have I done? I've married a man who doesn't love me. You love Laura and that's why I don't want to go to Peru with you. You don't love me and our marriage is all a hoax and as soon as you've had enough of me you'll cast me off . . . like an old shoe!'

An attack of hiccups prevented her from saying any more. She tried again to push free from him, but couldn't because she was exhausted. Physically and emotionally drained, she could only lie against him when he leaned back against the pillows, glad of his strength and the comfort of his fingers in her hair or against her cheek as he soothed her.

'I love you,' he said quietly and suddenly, and surprise robbed her of breath so that her hiccups stopped. 'I wouldn't be here if I didn't. I wouldn't have come back from Philadelphia if I didn't. I'd have flown straight to Peru from there if I didn't.' He paused and turned so that they were facing each other. 'If to want to be with you all the time, to share experiences with you, to share everything with you is to love you, then I love you.' He looked into her tear-drowned eyes, his own dark with emotion. 'Don't you believe me?' he whispered.

'I want to . . . but . . . but . . . you said on the way here that you wished you'd never met me,' she murmured, unable to keep to herself any more that wound which had hurt so much.

'I know,' he groaned. 'Because that was how I felt at that moment. I was hating you right then because you'd caused me more trouble, more sleepless nights and anxious days than any other woman I've ever met and then had decided to walk out of my life, discard me as if I meant no more to you than . . . than an old coat.' His mouth quirked with wry humour, but his fingers were gentle as he touched her cheek. 'When you walked away from me at the airport and hid yourself in the rest-room I went through hell. They were the worst moments of my life.' He drew a shaky breath. 'I didn't want to believe you might have tricked me. I didn't want to believe I might have married a cheat. At one time I would have said what the hell, shrugged it off, and gone on the flight to Miami, forgotten you. But I couldn't go. I had to wait around like any other lovesick fool, waiting for you to come out, wondering what it was I had to do to convince you that I'd married you in all sincerity with the intention of staying married to you.'

Margret didn't speak, guessing there was more to come. With her head on his shoulder she gazed up at the tough angle of his jaw profiled against the glow of lamplight and felt the first sharp thrill of possession.

'There was a time,' he went on, when I thought it was just what you'd called it, physical attraction, the same as I've felt for other women. I guessed you were only using my invitation to go to Peru to suit your own ends and had left Lindley's Point because you didn't want to come between Greg and Laura. My suspicions were confirmed when you ran off at Salem, so I decided to go away without you. I thought I could.' Bitterness edged his voice and for a while he was silent, tangling his fingers in her hair.

'But I couldn't get you out of my mind,' he continued in a low voice. 'I kept thinking about you in that meeting instead of attending to what everyone was saying about the project in Peru, and when I was asked if I would go back and take over the management of the project I couldn't give a straight answer. I realised I didn't want to go without you, I told them I would let them know and walked out, not sure what I was going to do next. I had a few drinks in a bar and that was when I found your cheque. I grabbed a taxi and went to the airport and waited on standby for the next flight to Boston, afraid that you might be gone before I got back and that I wouldn't know where to find you. I had to see you again. I had to have one more try, so I returned with the intention of. . . .' He broke off and slanted a glance at her, his mouth quirking.

'Of what?' she prompted, raising a finger to trace the scar at the corner of his mouth.

'Of seducing you. For what other reason would I visit you in your bedroom at one o'clock in the morning?' he mocked, his lips moving against the soft silkiness of the hair at her temple.

'Arrogant devil!' she accused, but her voice was soft.

'I found you were one step ahead of me and had already announced our forthcoming marriage to Greg, so I decided to make the most of the situation and propose to you. I did, and you accepted and I believed, I was almost sure, in fact, that you were sincere.'

'I was,' she whispered.

'Then why the attempt to run out on me today? And why accuse me of being in love with Laura? Where did you get that idea?'

'From her.'

'When?'

'This afternoon. She told me you'd only gone to Lindley's Point because she asked you to go there and check on me, find out if I was Greg's mistress or if I was going to marry him. She said you did it all for her and you told me once, yourself, that you felt you owed it to her to undo the harm you'd done to her by introducing Liza to Greg.'

'I went to Lindley's Point because I wanted to go

there,' Carl said flatly. 'My going there had nothing to do with Laura. Sure, she called me and asked me to go, but that was after I'd made arrangements to borrow Paul's boat. I didn't go there to please Laura or because I love her.'

'But you knew I was staying there.'

'I knew that some woman was staying there. Laura's description of you was very muddled and when I first saw you I was agreeably surprised. I was prepared to meet a scarlet woman.' Laughter shook his chest. 'Instead I was met by your version of Mary Poppins.'

'You lied to me!' Margret accused.

'I did? When?'

'That night. You said you wouldn't have broken into the house if you'd known I was staying there. And you did know I was staying there.'

'What I meant was that I wouldn't have entered unannounced—that's quite different from breaking in—if I'd known that the person staying there was like you,' he argued smoothly, turning to her and rubbing her nose with his.

'And you made me go cruising with you to get me out of the way while Laura and Greg met.'

'I *invited* you to go cruising with me because I wanted to get to know you better, and for no other reason, no matter what Laura told you. I did get to know you better, and so I asked you to fly with me to Peru.'

'To be your mistress,' she accused again.

'To be my love,' he retorted swiftly, and kissed her nose-tip. 'I'd still like you to go to Peru with me, but if you prefer to go to England I'll go there with you and take my chances. You're stuck with me now, you know. I love you and I'm not going to let you go anywhere without me. Do you believe me?'

'I want to,' she whispered. 'I want to believe you so badly.'

'God!' Impatience rasped in his voice as he lunged up on an elbow and loomed over her, his face drawn into savage lines, his eyes glittering with hostility. 'What else do I have to say or do to convince you? I've said more to you than I've ever said before to a woman.' His lips burned suddenly and agonisingly against her throat. 'Are you going to tell me you love Greg, after all? I won't believe you if you do.'

'No, oh no. I don't love Greg. I've never loved Greg. Whatever made you think that I do?' she exclaimed.

'Remember the night we arrived in Boston? You were very unhappy and I thought you might be regretting having left him.'

'So that was what you were referring to when you said I'd get over it? Oh, no, it wasn't that. I was unhappy because I was afraid to go away with you. I wanted to go with you, but I daren't take the risk because I was sure you didn't love me the way I loved you.'

'Are you still afraid?' he asked.

'Not as much as I was. But you have the power to hurt me and I suppose you always will have.'

'Remember you have that power too,' Carl said softly. 'You can and have hurt me, but I guess hurting one another is all part of learning to love. And that's what we've been doing these past two weeks, isn't it?'

'Yes, that's what we've been doing,' she agreed in a whisper.

'Then let's try again, shall we? Margret, will you fly with me to Peru tomorrow, to live with me there?'

'I'll fly with you anywhere,' she cried with joyous abandon, winding her arms about him and lifting her mouth willingly to his. And as his mouth crushed hers and another surge of passion threatened to drive everything from their minds except their need for each other she knew at last that love was not a dream or a spell woven by a magician. Love was real.

Take romance with you on your holiday.

Holiday time is almost here again. So look out for the special Mills & Boon Holiday Reading Pack.* Four new romances by four favourite authors. Attractive, smart, easy to pack and only £3.00.

*Available from 12th June.

Dakota Dreamin'
Janet Dailey

Forbidden Flame
Anne Mather

Devil Lover
Carole Mortimer

Gold to Remember
Mary Wibberley

 Mills & Boon

The rose of romance

Masquerade
Historical Romances

*Intrigue
excitement
romance*